Bond
No.1 for exam success

Non-verbal Reasoning
3D and Spatial
10 Minute Tests

CEM
(Durham University)

10–11⁺ years

OXFORD
UNIVERSITY PRESS

OXFORD
UNIVERSITY PRESS

Great Clarendon Street, Oxford, OX2 6DP, United Kingdom

Oxford University Press is a department of the University of Oxford.
It furthers the University's objective of excellence in research,
scholarship, and education by publishing worldwide. Oxford
is a registered trade mark of Oxford University Press in the UK
and in certain other countries

Text © Oxford University Press 2018

Author: Lynn Adams

British Library Cataloguing in Publication Data
Data available

978-0-19-276770-7

10 9 8 7 6 5 4 3 2 1

Paper used in the production of this book is a natural, recyclable
product made from wood grown in sustainable forests.
The manufacturing process conforms to the environmental
regulations of the country of origin.

Printed in the United Kingdom

Acknowledgements

Cover illustration: Lo Cole
Illustrations: Aptara
Page make-up: Aptara

Useful notes

In these tests and puzzles you'll be practising your **3D** and **spatial reasoning** skills.

Spatial reasoning is seeing and understanding the relationship between shapes and spaces. It involves looking at shapes and imagining them being joined together, taken apart, rotated, folded or viewed from different angles (for example, from the top or the side).

3D shapes

A three-dimensional (3D) shape is solid rather than flat (which is 2D). We call it 3D because it can be measured in three directions: width, depth and height.

3D shapes, including cubes, can be rotated in different **planes**.

When you rotate something by keeping the base of the shape on the ground, you are rotating on the *plane of the ground* (turning it left or right, clockwise or anticlockwise).

If an object rotates on a *side face*, it turns from front to back or bottom to top (away from you) or back to front or top to bottom (towards you).

Plane of the page means the flat surface of the page. The shape will turn on its back face, clockwise or anticlockwise.

For example:

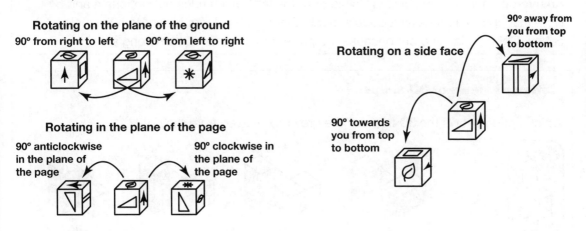

Nets of 3D shapes

A **net** is a flat shape (2D) that can be folded to make a 3D shape. Imagine a net being folded **into** the page, as shown below. This means that you fold the **faces** (the surfaces) of the net *away* from you.

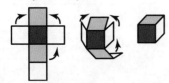

Question examples

Here are some examples of the different types of 3D and spatial reasoning questions that appear in this book, followed by the answers. Read through each example before you start the tests.

When you have eliminated all but one of the options, always check that the option left *is* possible. (You may have made a mistake and wrongly rejected an option!)

For the question types on this page you may be asked to identify the view from *above, left, right* or *back*.

2D views of 3D shapes

Which option shows a 2D view of the 3D figure from the *left*?

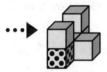

                          a   **b**   **c**   **d**

Answer: c There are five blocks visible from the left, which rules out options a and b. Note that option a contains a double block, that is, a block equivalent to two single cubes. Option d is ruled out because the patterned block is on the wrong side.

Different views of 3D shapes

Which option shows the 3D figure in the grey box viewed from the *right*?

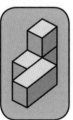

                                a   **b**   **c**   **d**

Answer: a Option b is ruled out because the 2-cube block is in the wrong position. Options c and d are ruled out because there are no 2-cube blocks. (Note: a 2-cube block is a single block that is equivalent in size to two cubes.)

3D rotation

Which of the 3D figures in the grey box has been **rotated** to make the new 3D figure?

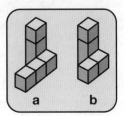

Answer: b Figure a can be rejected because it has the wrong number of cubes. Figure b has been rotated 90° to the right (anticlockwise) and then 90° *away* from you.

Building blocks

Which set of blocks can be put together to make the 3D figure on the left?

Answer: a Options b and c can be rejected because the shape on the left is made from two 2-cube blocks and one single cube. A 2-cube block is rotated 90° in the plane of the page and sits on top of the single cube. A second 2-cube block moves to the front.

Complete the shape

Which option can be added to the blocks in the grey box to create an exact copy of the 3D figure below? (Note: You may need to use rotation.)

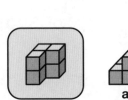

Answer: b There are ten cubes in the 3D figure above. You need four more cubes to add to the blocks on the left, so options c and d can be rejected. Option b rotates 90° clockwise in the plane of the page and fits to the front and right of the figure.

Question examples (continued)

Nets and cubes

Which cube can be made from the net?

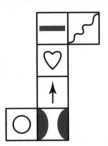

a   b   c   d

Answer: d You can rule out Options a and b because the arrow should point to the base of the heart. Option c is ruled out because the net does not have a grey square.

Partial nets

Which of the partial nets can be folded to make the cube shown?

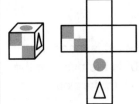 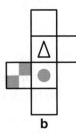 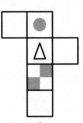 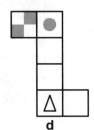

a   b   c   d

Answer: a Options b and d are ruled out because the triangle should point to the circle, and with nothing in between. Option c is ruled out because the circle and checked pattern should not be on opposite sides. (They should be on adjacent sides.)

Shaded nets

Which of the 3D shapes can be made from the shaded net on the left?

a   b   c   d

Answer: d Options a, b and c are ruled out because the rectangular faces should *not* be shaded.

Cube views

The figures on the left are three views of the same cube. Which option should replace the **blank** cube face?

a   b   c   d

Answer: d The arrow always points to the circle.

Fold along the line

Which option shows the figure in the grey box when folded along the dotted line?

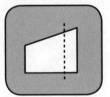

a   b   c   d

Answer: b Options c and d can be rejected because they are not folded. The folded part of option a is too narrow. In option b, the part of the figure to the right side of the dotted line is folded towards you.

Fold and punch

A shape is folded and then one or more holes is punched, as shown in the grey box. Which answer shows the correct shape when it is unfolded?

a   b   c   d

Answer: b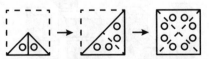

Test 1

Which set of blocks can be put together to make the 3D figure on the left?

1

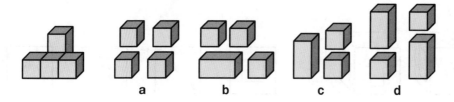

a   b   c   d   _____   1

2

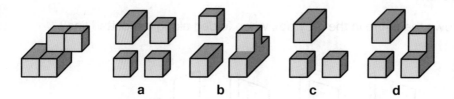

a   b   c   d   _____   1

3

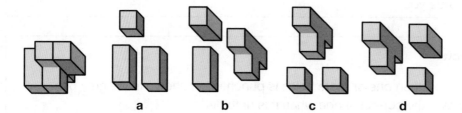

a   b   c   d   _____   1

4

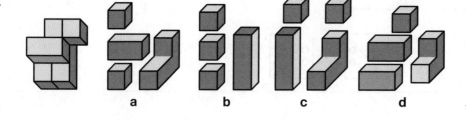

a   b   c   d   _____   1

Which option can be added to the blocks in the grey box to create an exact copy of the 3D figure below, without using rotation?

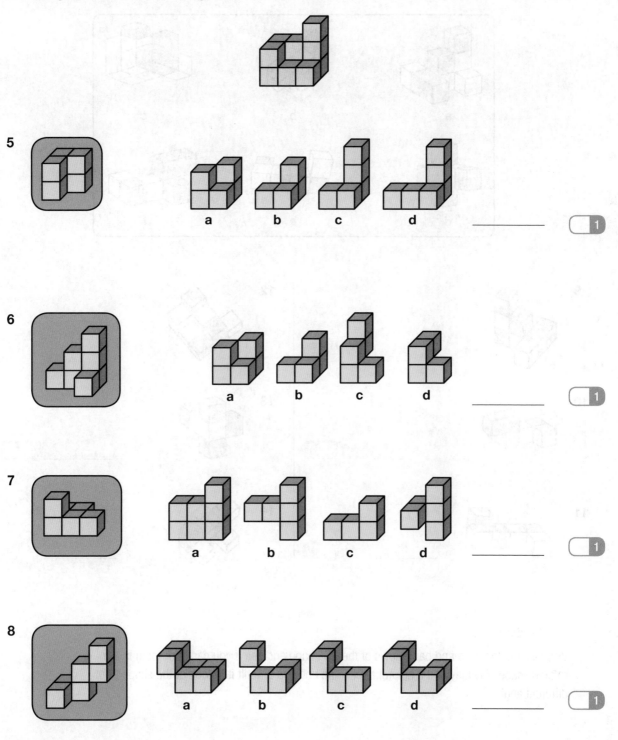

5

a   b   c   d   _____   1

6

a   b   c   d   _____   1

7

a   b   c   d   _____   1

8

a   b   c   d   _____   1

Which of the 3D figures in the grey box has been **rotated** to make the new 3D figure?

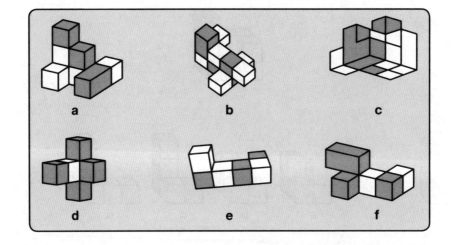

a

b

c

d

e

f

9

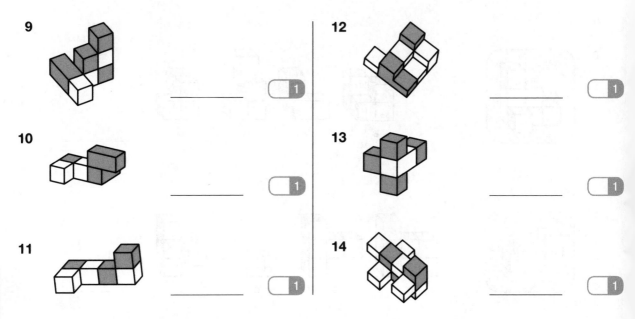

_____ (1)

10

_____ (1)

11

_____ (1)

12

_____ (1)

13

_____ (1)

14

_____ (1)

> ### 3D Rotation Tip!
>
> Visualise the top, side and back views of the 3D shape and see if you can spot them in the rotated shape. You may find it helpful to pick the book up and tilt it to look at the shape from different angles.

Which option shows the figure in the grey box when folded along the dotted line?

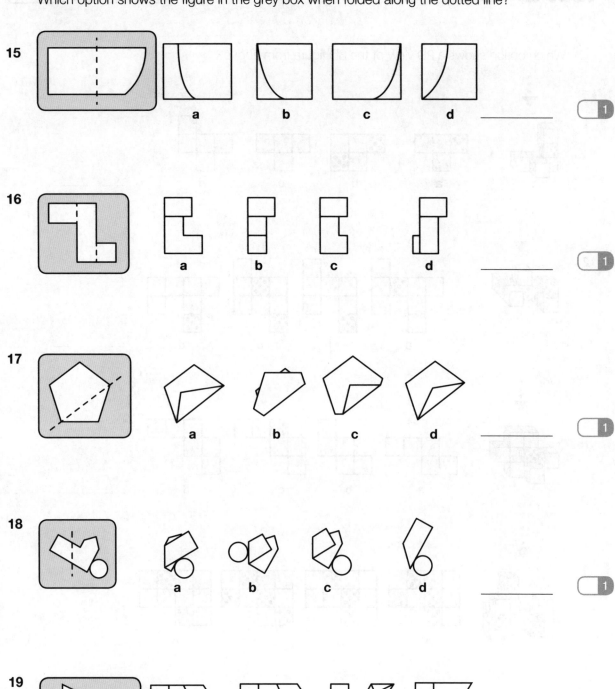

15   a   b   c   d   _____   1

16   a   b   c   d   _____   1

17   a   b   c   d   _____   1

18   a   b   c   d   _____   1

19   a   b   c   d   _____   1

Total   19

Which option shows a 2D view of the 3D figure from *above*?

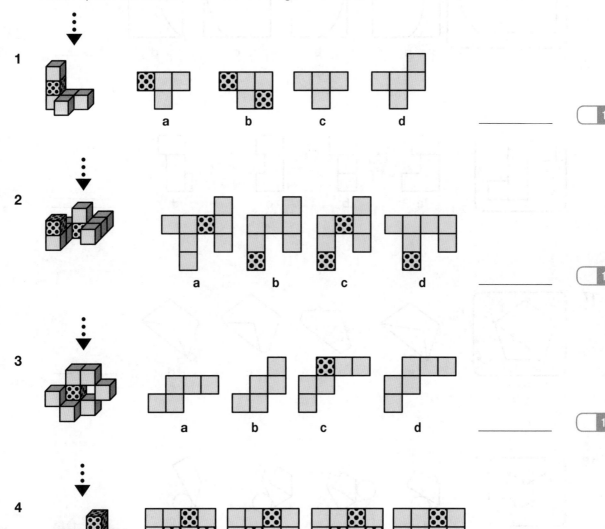

1   a   b   c   d   1

2   a   b   c   d   1

3   a   b   c   d   1

4   a   b   c   d   1

Looking at 3D Shapes Tip!

You can look at a 3D shape from different views. The *back* view is what you see if you are standing directly behind the shape. The *side* view is what you see if you are standing directly to one side (right or left) of the shape. The *top* view is what you see if you are hovering directly above the shape looking down on it.

A shape is folded and then one or more holes is punched, as shown in the grey box. Which answer shows the correct shape when it is unfolded?

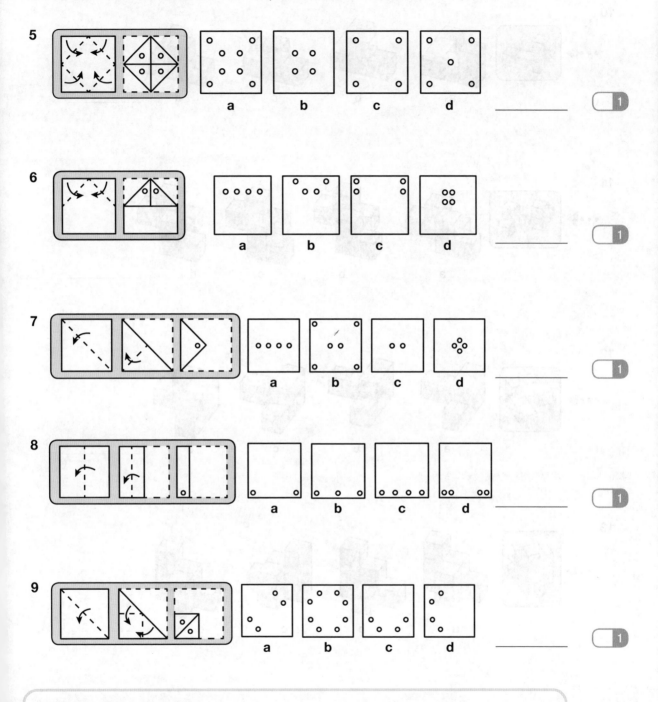

5   a   b   c   d   _____   1

6   a   b   c   d   _____   1

7   a   b   c   d   _____   1

8   a   b   c   d   _____   1

9   a   b   c   d   _____   1

Folding and Punching Tip!

When solving these questions, work backwards! Unfold the shape step-by-step, from the last step to the first. It can help to draw in the holes as you go.

Which option shows the 3D figure in the grey box viewed from the *left*?

10

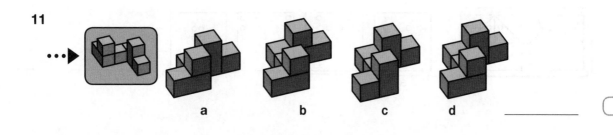

a   b   c   d _____ 1

11

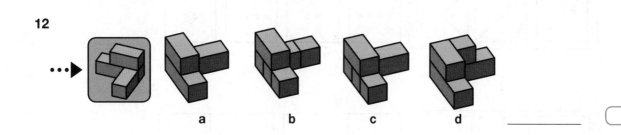

a   b   c   d _____ 1

12

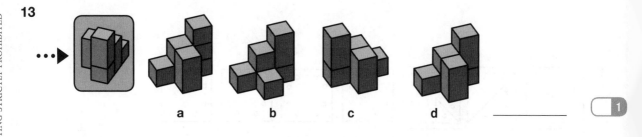

a   b   c   d _____ 1

13

a   b   c   d _____ 1

Which cube can be made from the net?

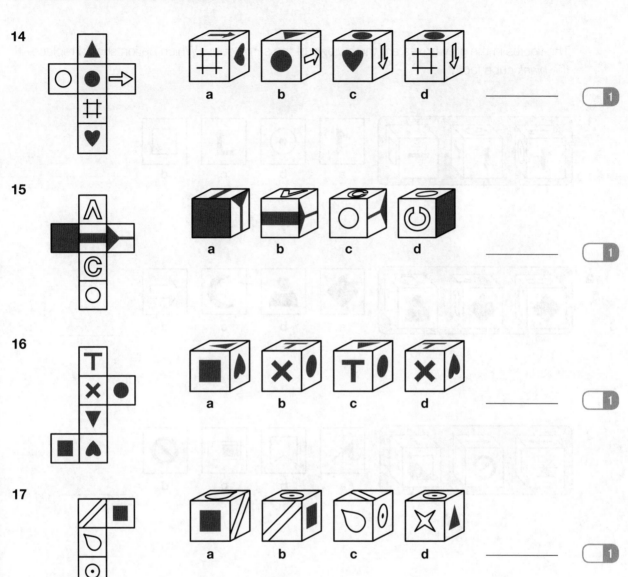

14

a   b   c   d _____ ◯1

15

a   b   c   d _____ ◯1

16

a   b   c   d _____ ◯1

17

a   b   c   d _____ ◯1

> **Nets and Cubes Tip!**
>
> Look for the obvious first– make sure all of the shapes on the cubes are actually on the net!
> Then decide which shapes are *opposite* each other – you can eliminate any options where these
> shapes are *next* to each other.

Total ▢ 17

Test 3

 Test time: 0 — 5 — 10 minutes

The figures in the grey boxes are three views of the same cube. Which option should replace the *blank* cube face?

1
a b c d _____ 1

2
a b c d _____

3
a b c d _____

4
a b c d _____

Which of the 3D shapes can be made from the shaded net in the grey box?

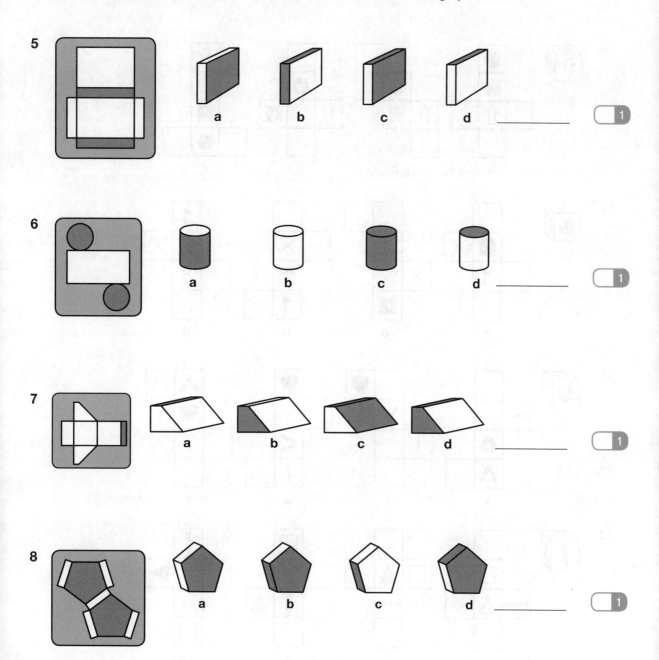

5
 a b c d _____ 1

6
 a b c d _____ 1

7
 a b c d _____ 1

8
 a b c d _____ 1

Which of the partial nets can be folded to make the cube shown?

9

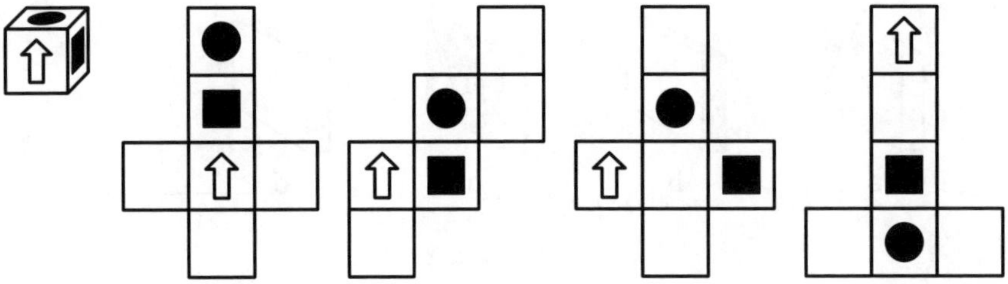

a   b   c   d _____

10

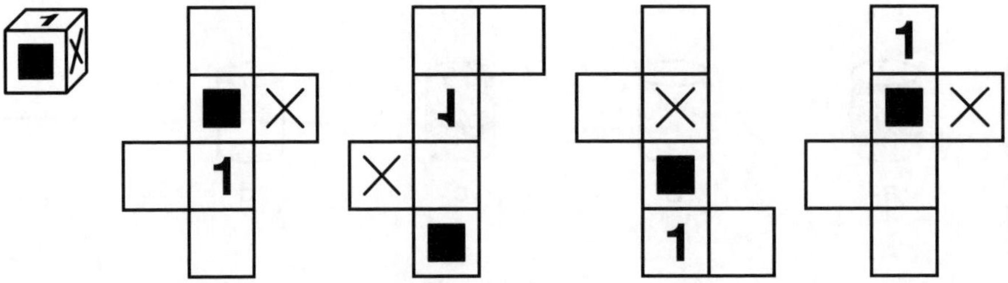

a   b   c   d _____

11

a   b   c   d _____

12

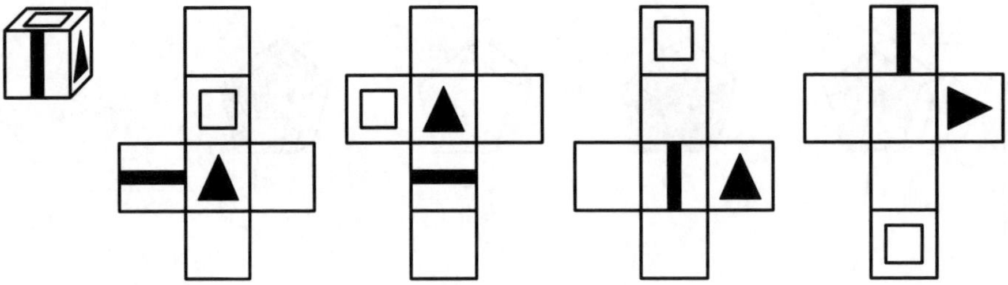

a   b   c   d _____

Nets and Cubes Tip!

Check for any symbol on the cube that points towards another symbol – it must point towards the same symbol on the net for it to be the correct answer.

Which option shows a 2D view of the 3D figure from the *left*?

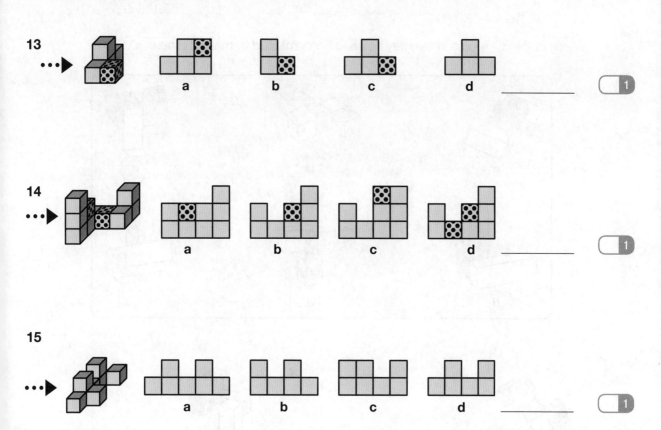

13

a b c d _____ (1)

14

a b c d _____ (1)

15

a b c d _____ (1)

16

a b c d _____ (1)

Test 4

Which of the 3D figures in the grey box has been **rotated** to make the *new* 3D figure?

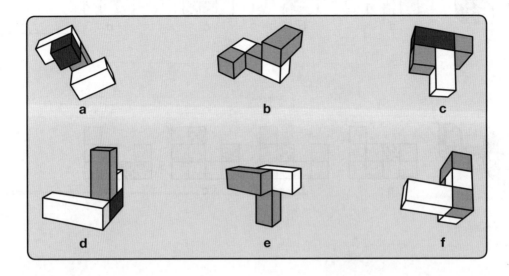

a   b   c

d   e   f

1   _____ (1)

2   _____ (1)

3   _____ (1)

4   _____ (1)

5   _____ (1)

6   _____ (1)

Which set of blocks can be put together to make the 3D figure on the left?

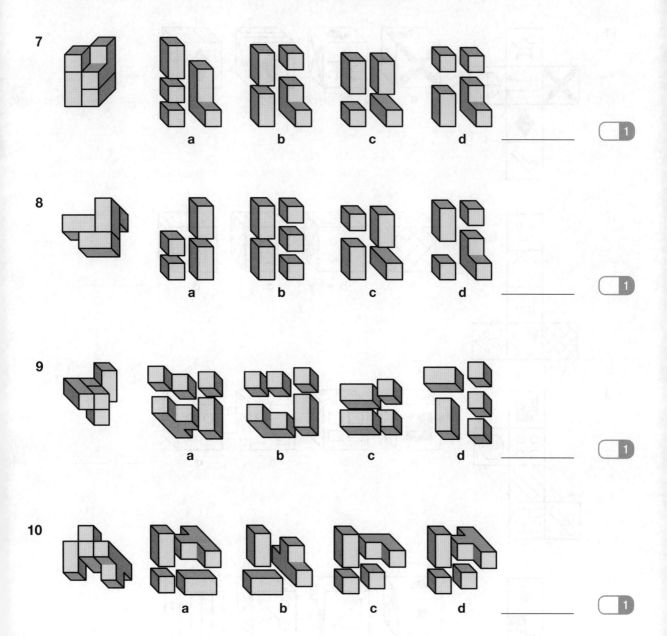

7

a   b   c   d _____ (1

8

a   b   c   d _____ (1

9

a   b   c   d _____ (1

10

a   b   c   d _____ (1

Which cube can be made from the net?

11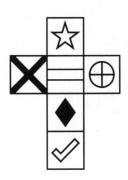
a   b   c   d   _____ ⬭1

12
a   b   c   d   _____ ⬭1

13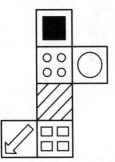
a   b   c   d   _____ ⬭1

14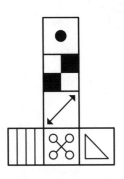
a   b   c   d   _____ ⬭1

Which option shows the figure in the grey box when folded along the dotted line?

15

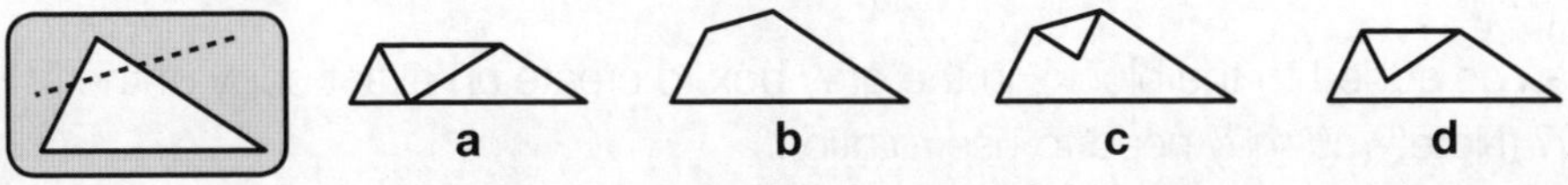

a   b   c   d

16

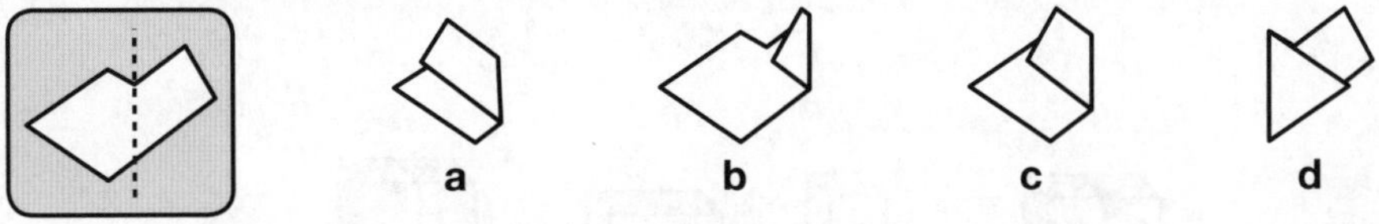

a   b   c   d

17

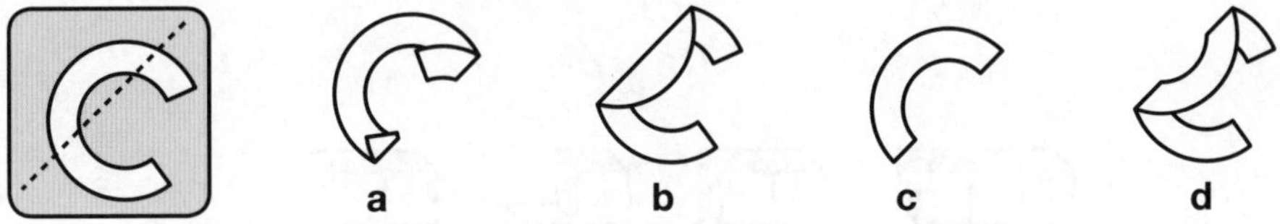

a   b   c   d

18

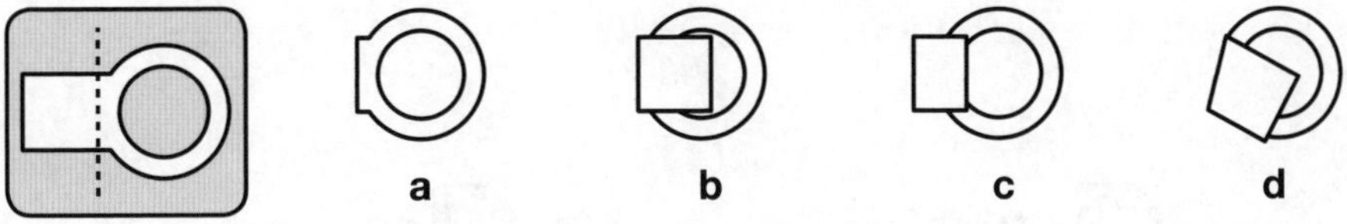

a   b   c   d

19

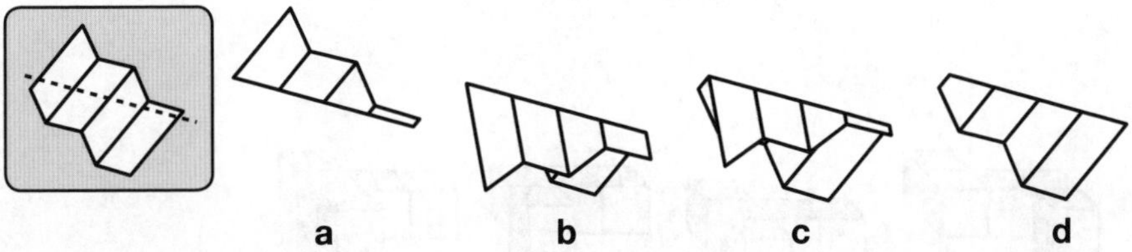

a   b   c   d

Total   19

23

Test 5

Which option can be added to the blocks in the grey box to create an exact copy of the 3D figure below? (Note: You may need to use rotation.)

1

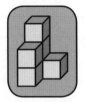
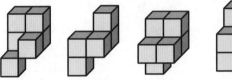

a   b   c   d   _____   1

2

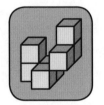
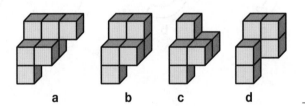

a   b   c   d   _____   1

3

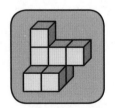
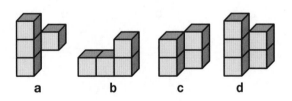

a   b   c   d   _____   1

4

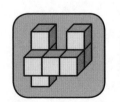
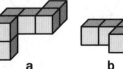

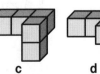

a   b   c   d   _____   1

Which option shows the 3D figure in the grey box viewed from the *back*?

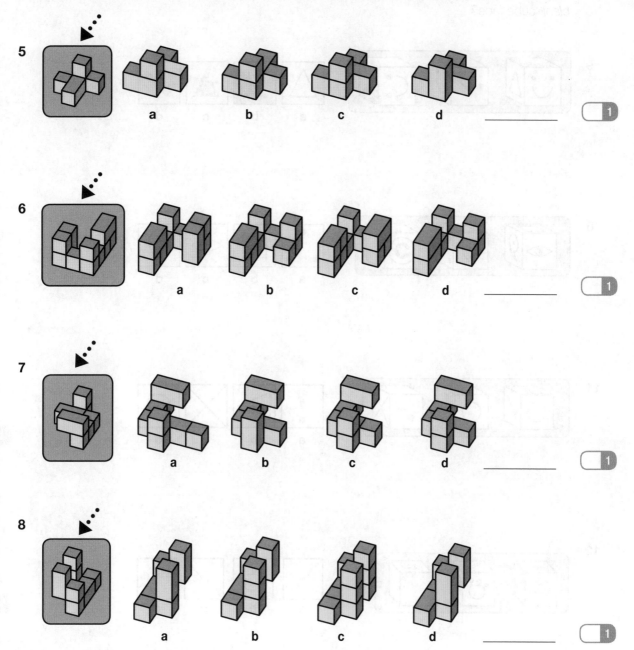

5

a   b   c   d   _____   1

6

a   b   c   d   _____   1

7

a   b   c   d   _____   1

8

a   b   c   d   _____   1

The figures in the grey boxes are three views of the same cube. Which option should replace the *blank* cube face?

9

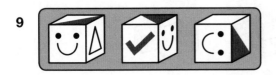 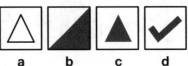

a   b   c   d   _____

10

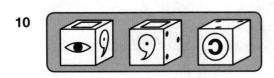 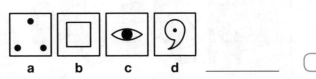

a   b   c   d   _____ 1

11

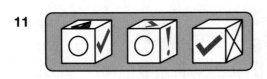 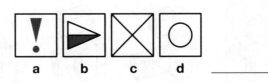

a   b   c   d   _____ 1

12

 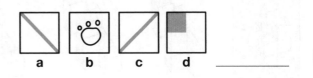

a   b   c   d   _____ 1

Which of the 3D shapes can be made from the shaded net on the left?

13

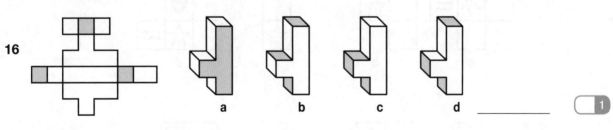

a   b   c   d _____ ◯ 1

14

a   b   c   d _____ ◯ 1

15

a   b   c   d _____ ◯ 1

16

a   b   c   d _____ ◯ 1

Total   16

Test 6

Which of the partial nets can be folded to make the cube shown?

1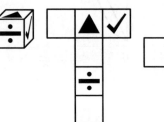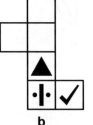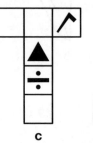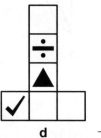

  a   b   c   d

2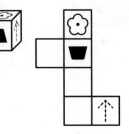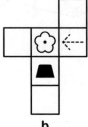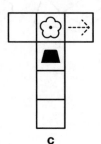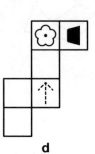

  a   b   c   d

3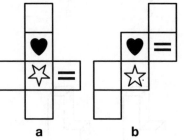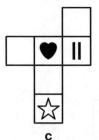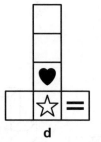

  a   b   c   d

4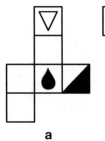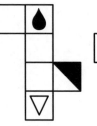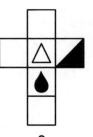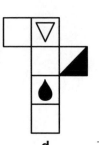

  a   b   c   d

A shape is folded and then one or more holes is punched, as shown in the grey box.
Which option shows the correct shape when it is unfolded?

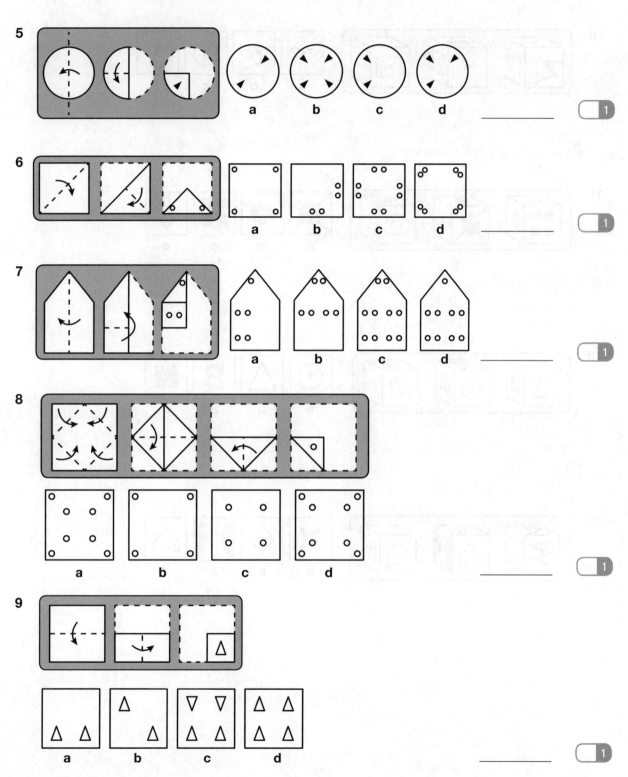

5   a   b   c   d   1

6   a   b   c   d   1

7   a   b   c   d   1

8   a   b   c   d   1

9   a   b   c   d   1

The figures in the grey boxes are three views of the same cube. Which option should replace the *blank* cube face?

10

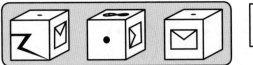 

a   b   c   d   _____ [1]

11

 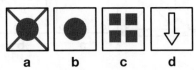

a   b   c   d   _____ [1]

12

 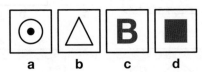

a   b   c   d   _____ [1]

13

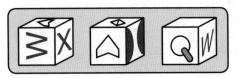 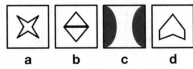

a   b   c   d   _____ [1]

Which option shows the 3D figure in the grey box viewed from the *left*?

14

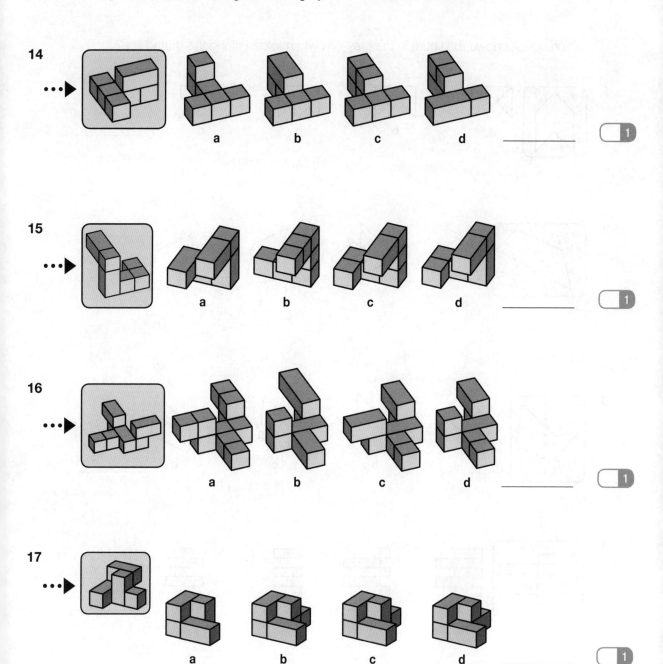

a   b   c   d _____ ⬭ 1

15

a   b   c   d _____ ⬭ 1

16

a   b   c   d _____ ⬭ 1

17

a   b   c   d _____ ⬭ 1

Total ⬭ 17

Test 7

Which option shows the figure in the grey box when folded along the dotted line?

1 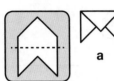 **a**   **b**   **c**   **d**   1

2 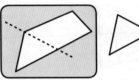 **a**   **b**   **c**   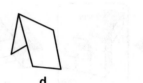 **d**   1

3   **a**   **b**   **c**   **d**   1

4 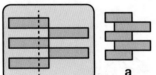 **a**   **b**   **c**   **d**   1

5 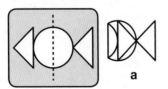 **a**   **b**   **c**   **d**   1

Which set of blocks can be put together to make the 3D figure on the left?

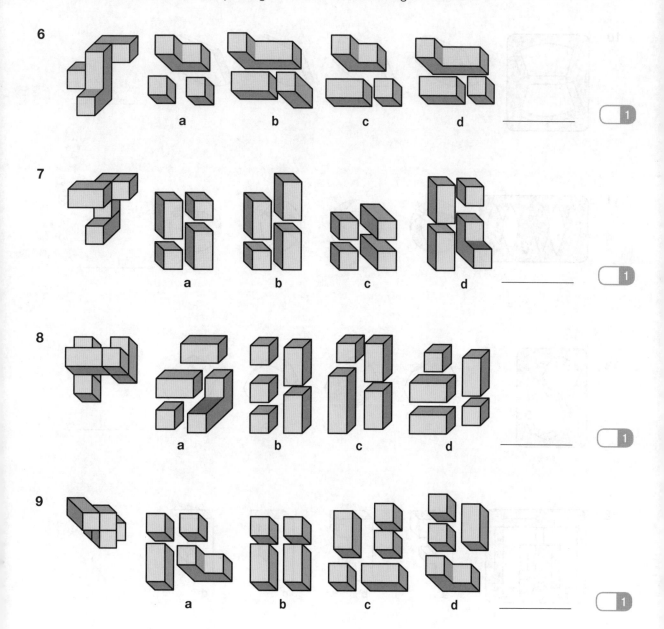

6   a   b   c   d   _____ 1

7   a   b   c   d   _____ 1

8   a   b   c   d   _____ 1

9   a   b   c   d   _____ 1

Building Blocks Tip!

Look at the individual blocks carefully. Count the number of cubes so you can rule out any options with the wrong number of cubes. Also look at the shapes of the blocks. Are there cubes, cuboids or 'L' shapes? You can rule out any options where these are different.

Which of the 3D shapes can be made from the shaded net in the grey box?

10

a   b   c   d _____ 1

11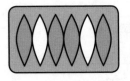

a   b   c   d _____ 1

12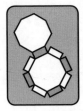

a   b   c   d _____ 1

13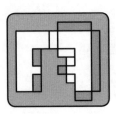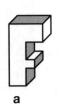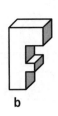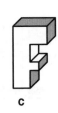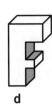

a   b   c   d _____ 1

Which option can be added to the blocks in the grey box to create an exact copy of the 3D figure below?

14

  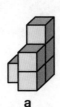 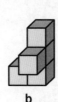 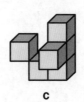 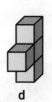

a   b   c   d _____ 1

15

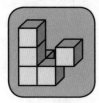   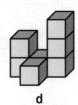

a   b   c   d _____ 1

16

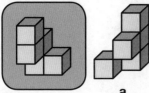 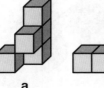 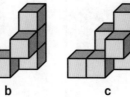 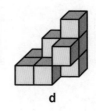

a   b   c   d _____ 1

17

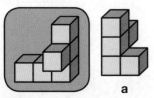   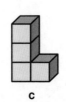

a   b   c   d _____ 1

Total 17

Which of the 3D figures in the grey box has been **rotated** to make the new 3D figure?

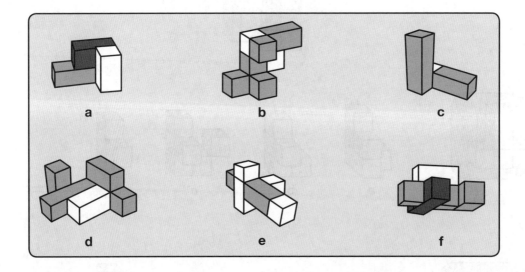

a   b   c

d   e   f

1 _____ 1

4 _____ 1

2 _____ 1

5 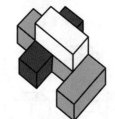 _____ 1

3  _____ 1

6 _____ 1

A shape is folded and then one or more holes is punched, as shown in the grey box.
Which option shows the correct shape when it is unfolded?

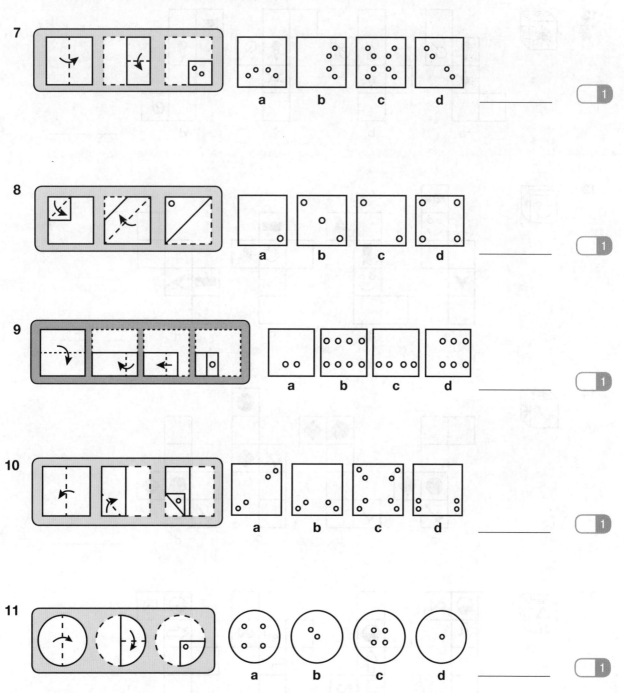

7

a   b   c   d _____ 1

8

a   b   c   d _____ 1

9

a   b   c   d _____ 1

10

a   b   c   d _____ 1

11

a   b   c   d _____ 1

Which of the partial nets can be folded to make the cube shown?

12

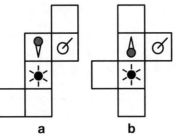 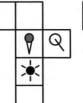 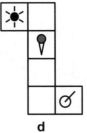

a   b   c   d

13

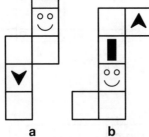 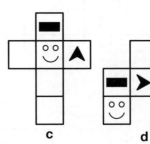 

a   b   c   d

14

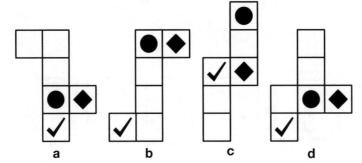

a   b   c   d

15

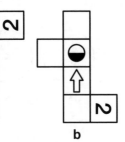 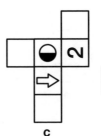 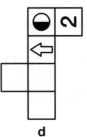

a   b   c   d

Test continues after Answers section →

Answers

Test 1
(pages 8–11)

1 b The 2-cube block is rotated 90° and is at the back of the figure. The three single cubes are at the front of the figure.

2 d The top left block drops down to the left side of the 'L'-shaped block. The cube moves up to the top right of the 'L'-shaped block.

3 b The top left block moves to the right side of the 'T'-shaped block. The bottom left block moves to the left of the 'T' shape.

4 a The 'L'-shaped block rotates towards you and the rectangular block goes in front of the 'L' shape. One cube is then placed on the top right and the second cube on the bottom left.

5 c You need three cubes for the back layer and two for the front layer.

Option c fits to the right side of the shape.

6 d You need three cubes for the front layer and one for the left middle of the back layer.

Option d fits to the left side of the shape.

7 b You just need cubes for the back layer; a tower of three for the right side and some for the middle row.

Option b fits to the back, right side of the shape.

8 d You need one cube for the bottom right and one for the middle left of the back layer, and three cubes for the front layer.

Option d slides onto the front of the shape.

9 a Look for steps with a 2-cube block at the bottom. Shape a has been rotated 90° from right to left.

10 f You need two double grey blocks and three single cubes, so the answer must be option f. Shape f has been rotated 180° on its base.

11 e You need a twisted 'C' shape, so the answer must be option e. Shape e has been rotated 90° towards you from top to bottom.

12 c You need a grey 3-cube 'L' shape, so the answer must be option c. Shape c has been rotated 90° towards you from top to bottom.

13 d You need three single grey cubes on the faces of a white block, so the answer must be option d. Shape d has been rotated 180° on its base.

14 b This has a lot of alternate grey and white cubes, so the answer must be option b. Shape b has been rotated 180° on its base.

15 b Options a and d are ruled out because the top of the figure is folded in half, so the curve should meet the corner of the rectangle. Option c is rejected because the curve goes the wrong way.

16 b Options a and c are ruled out because the bottom section hasn't been folded. Option d is ruled out because the folded bottom part must fit exactly onto the vertical.

17 d Option a is ruled out because the folded part is not a symmetric shape. Options b and c are ruled out because they are not folded on the vertices of the pentagon.

18 c Option a is ruled out because the fold is on the top corner of the 'L' shape. Option b is ruled out because you could not have a fold next to the circle. Option d is ruled out because the top part should end in a point.

19 b Option a is ruled out because the horizontal piece is too narrow. Option c is rejected because the folds are too high. Option d is ruled out because the top right has been cut off, not folded.

Test 2
(pages 12–15)

1 c There are four blocks visible from the top, which rules out options b and d. You can't see the patterned block from above, so option a is also ruled out.

2 b There is only one patterned block visible from above, which rules out option c. The patterned block is not in the centre row, so option a can be rejected. Option d does not have three blocks on the right, so it can be rejected.

3 a All the blocks visible from above will be plain, which rules out option c. There will be two blocks in the front row and three blocks behind them, which rules out options b and d.

4 b Options a and c are ruled out because only three patterned blocks are visible from above. Option d is ruled out because there are only two patterned blocks.

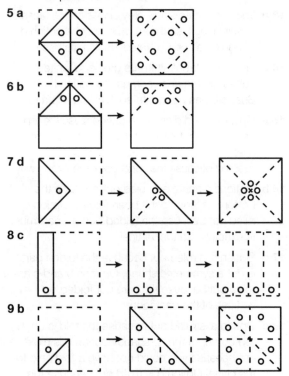

5 a

6 b

7 d

8 c

9 b

10 b Option a is ruled out because the single cube on top should be in the centre, not the on left. On the right of the figure there should be a 2-cube block with a single cube behind. This rules out options c and d.

11 d The single centre cube is missing from option a, so it is ruled out. Option b is ruled out because there should be a single cube on the back bottom right of the figure. Option c is ruled out because the 2-cube block at the front should be horizontal not vertical.

12 a Options b and c are ruled out because the bottom row is not made up of separate cubes. Option d is ruled out because it has an extra cube on the top row.

13 d Option a is ruled out because it has three separate cubes to the back right of the figure. Option b is ruled out because the block at the front middle should be two cubes tall. Option c is ruled out because when looking from the left the tallest block should be on the right side of the figure.

14 d Option a has a black arrow, but the arrow on the net is white, so this option is ruled out. Option b is ruled out because the triangle should be pointing away from the black circle, not towards it. Option c is ruled out because the black circle and the heart must be on opposite sides, not next to each other.

15 c Option a is ruled out because the shaded face must be opposite the shaded triangle with the line. Option b is ruled out because the 'V' shape should be pointing away from the stripe. Option d is ruled out because the dot should be facing the side of the 'C' shape, not the opening.

16 b Option a is ruled out because the tip of the triangle should be pointing towards the tip of the heart. Options c and d can be ruled out because the bar of the 'T' shape should face the top of the heart.

17 a You can rule out options b and c because the circle must be opposite the stripe, not next to it. Option d is ruled out because the triangle should be to the left of the star when the circle is on top.

Test 3

(pages 16–19)

1 b Options a and d can be ruled out because you can see them on the third cube. Option c can be rejected because that would be on the left vertical face of cube 3. Cube 3 is cube 1 rotated 90° anticlockwise in the plane of the page.

2 a Options b and d can be ruled out because you can see them on the third cube. The arrow has the crescent 'beneath' it and the diamond to its left. Cube 3 is cube 1 rotated 90° clockwise in the plane of the ground.

3 d From cubes 1 and 2 you can see the cross with the triangle is opposite the circle with the line, and the 'i' is opposite the ribbon (the square is their base). The face to the right of the 'i' is the circle with the line. Cube 3 is cube 1 rotated 90° clockwise in the plane of the ground, then rotated 90° away from you.

4 c Reject option d because you can see it on the cube. From cubes 1 and 2 you can see the square with the cross is opposite the rectangle with lines and the aeroplane is opposite the envelope. The required option is the base of cube 2. Cube 3 is cube 2 rotated 90° away from you.

5 d Options a and c are ruled out because the large rectangular faces should not be shaded. Option b is ruled out because narrow shaded faces should not be next to each other.

6 d Options a and c are ruled out because the cylinder face should not be shaded. Option b is ruled out because the top circular face should be shaded.

7 a Options b, c and d are ruled out because the only shaded face should be the top one.

8 a Options b, c and d are ruled out because no rectangular face should be shaded.

9 b Option a is ruled out because the arrow should point to the circle, not the square. Options c and d are ruled out because the arrow and square must be next to each other, not on opposite sides.

10 d Options a, and b are ruled out because the base of the number 1 should be closest to the square. Option b is ruled out because the 1 and the square should be next to each other, not on opposite faces. Option c is ruled out because the 1 is to the left of the cross.

11 a Options b, c and d are ruled out because the tip of the 'V' shape must point towards the top of the heart.

12 d Options b and c are ruled out because a point of the triangle should point to the square. Option a is ruled out because the stripe should not point to the triangle.

13 d Options a, b and c are ruled out because from the left view the patterned block is not visible.

14 b Option a can be rejected because the second column should have only one block. Option c is ruled out because the third column should have only two blocks. Option d is ruled out because only one patterned block is visible from the left.

15 a Options b, c and d are ruled out because there should be five blocks in the bottom row.

16 c Option d is ruled out because there are only two blocks in the bottom row. Options a and b are ruled out because only eight blocks are visible from the left.

Test 4
(pages 20–23)

1 b You only need grey and white blocks, so options a, c and d can be rejected. Option b is the only one with one 2-cube grey block. Shape b has been rotated 90° away from you from bottom to top.

2 d You need a 2-cube black block so options a, b, e and f can be rejected. Option d has a 3-cube white block next to the black one. Shape d has been rotated 180° on its base, then away from you.

3 e You only need three 2-cube blocks, so the answer must be option e. Shape e has been rotated 180° on its base.

4 a You need a black block so options b, e and f can be rejected. The other blocks make a backward 'S' shape, so the answer must be option a. Shape a has been rotated 90° clockwise in the plane of the page.

5 f There are no black blocks so options a, c and d can be rejected. You need one white double block and two single white blocks, ruling out options b and e. So the answer must be option f. Shape f has been rotated 90° from left to right.

6 c You need one double black block and two grey blocks, so the answer must be option c. Shape c has been rotated 180° on its base.

7 b You need a 3-cube 'L'-shaped piece, so options a and c can be rejected. Option d can be rejected because you need two 2-cube blocks.

8 c You need three 2-cube blocks, so options a, b and d can be ruled out.

9 d The three cubes are in the middle of the figure with the 2-cube blocks either side.

10 a Option c can be ruled out because there is no 'T'-shaped piece. You need two double-length blocks and one single cube, so options b and d can be rejected. The 'T' shape is rotated 90° anticlockwise in the plane of the page. The bottom right 2-cube block sits to the left of the 'T' shape with a cube on top. The other 2-cube block sits on the left of the figure.

11 a Option b is ruled out because the diamond and the star shape must be on opposite sides. Option c is ruled out because the stripe and the tick shape must be on opposite sides, not next to each other. Option d is ruled out because the stripe should be pointing to the circle with the cross inside.

12 c Option a is ruled out because the top of the glass should face the letter 'B'. Option b is ruled out because the mouth of the smiley face should face away from the white circle. Option d is ruled out because the chevrons (the two sideways 'V' shapes) should point towards the circle, not the 'B'.

13 b Option a is ruled out because the diagonal stripes and the shaded square must be on opposite sides. Option c is ruled out because the circle must be opposite the arrow, not next to it. Option d is ruled out because the arrow must point towards the four dots, not away from them.

14 c Option a is ruled out because the triangle on the net is white, not shaded as it is on this cube. Option b is ruled out because the double-ended arrow should point to the space opposite the white triangle, not the tip of the triangle. Option d is ruled out because the three stripes should point towards the dot.

15 c Options a and d are ruled out because the top will not be horizontal. Option b is ruled out because the top has been cut off rather than folded.

16 a All the fold lines are vertical, so all options are still possible. Options b and d are ruled out because the fold is not at the corner of the top indent. Option c is rejected because the folded right-hand side should project beyond the left edge.

17 d Option c is ruled out because it has been cut, not folded. Option a is ruled out because the fold is too low down. Option b is ruled out because the fold is too high up.

18 b Option a is ruled out because the figure has been cut, not folded. Option d can be ruled out because the fold is diagonal not vertical. Option c is rejected because the fold is too far to the left.

19 c Options a and d are ruled out because the figure has been cut not folded. Option b is ruled out because too much of the right-hand panel is folded down.

Test 5
(pages 24–27)

1 d You need three cubes for the top right corner of the back layer and three in an upside-down 'L' for the front layer.

Option d fits onto the right side of the figure.

2 b You need two cubes for the top row of the back layer and three in an upside-down 'L' for the front layer.

Option b fits onto the left side of the figure.

3 d You need three cubes for the back layer and two for the front layer. None of these seem to fit, so try rotating them.

Option d is rotated 90° anticlockwise in the plane of the page. It then fits onto the front of the figure.

4 c You need one cube for the top middle of the back layer (and possibly the two cubes beneath it – depending on what is hidden), and two for the bottom left of the front layer. Nothing seems to fit, so try rotation.

Option c is rotated 90° clockwise and slides in from underneath.

5 b They are all the right shape, so you need to look at the individual blocks. Options a, c and d are ruled out because the part projecting forward (in the original) is a single 2-cube block.

6 a Options b, c and d can be rejected because the top layer should have three cubes and one double block.

7 d Option a is ruled out because there is an extra cube on the lower right. Option b is ruled out because there should be two cubes on top of each other at the front. Option c is ruled out because the single cube on the bottom layer should be to the left of the double block, not to the right of it.

8 b Options c and d are ruled out because there should be a double block in the middle of the left side bottom row. Option a is also ruled out because the back column (on the original) has a single cube at the top.

9 d Option b can be rejected because the shaded half-square is already visible. We can see the tick is to the left of the smiley face and adjacent to the shaded half-square. Cube 3 is cube 1 rotated 90° clockwise in the plane of the page.

10 b Option a can be rejected because the three dots are already visible. Option d can be rejected because the '9' is adjacent to the base of the three dots. Option c can be rejected because the first two cubes show us the eye is opposite the three dots. Cube 3 is cube 2 rotated 90° anticlockwise in the plane of the page, then rotated 180° on its base.

11 b Option c can be rejected because the cross is already visible. Option d can be rejected because the circle is to the left of the tick. Option a can be rejected because the exclamation mark is under the tick. Cube 3 is cube 1 rotated 90° right to left.

12 c Option d can be rejected because the shaded quarter-square is already visible. Cubes 1 and 2 show us the shaded quarter-square is opposite the paw print, so option b can be rejected. The diagonal stripe does not go to the vertex joining the shaded quarter-square and '@' sign, so option a can be rejected. Cube 3 is cube 1 rotated 90° right to left and then 90° away from you from top to bottom.

13 c Options a and b are ruled out because the triangular faces should not be shaded. Option d is ruled out because the small rectangular face should not be shaded.

14 a Options b and d are ruled out because the smallest rectangular face should not be shaded. Option c is ruled out because the pentagon should not be shaded.

15 b Option a is ruled out because there should not be two shaded faces next to each other. Options c and d are ruled out because there should not be two white faces next to each other.

16 d Option a is ruled out because the 'T'-shaped face should not be shaded. Options b and c are ruled out because the top face of the cube should not be shaded.

Test 6

(pages 28–31)

1 c Option a is ruled out because the triangle and division sign should be next to each other, not on opposite sides. Option b is ruled out because the division sign should be in the

same orientation as the tick. Option d is ruled out because the division sign should be next to the base of the triangle, not a point.

2 b Option a is ruled out because the curved part of the trapezium should be nearest the flower. Option c is ruled out because the arrow should point towards the flower. Option d is ruled out because the flower and arrow should be next to each other, not on opposite sides.

3 d Option a is ruled out because a point of the star should be pointing at the point of the heart. Option b is ruled out because the two lines should point towards the star. Option c is ruled out because the heart and star should be on adjacent sides.

4 b Options a and d are ruled out because the triangle and tear drop shape should be on adjacent sides . Option c is ruled out because the tip of the triangle should point to the tip of the tear drop shape.

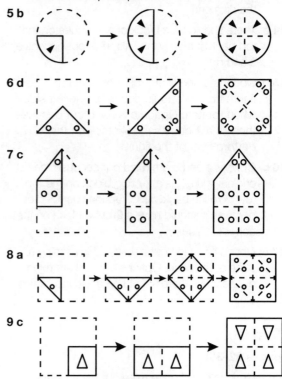

5 b

6 d

7 c

8 a

9 c

10 a Option d can be rejected because the dot is already visible. Option b can be rejected because the zigzag is to the left of the envelope. Cubes 1 and 2 show us the figure of eight is opposite the zigzag. It must be option a – and the orientation of the figure of eight is correct. Cube 3 is cube 2 rotated 90° away from you top to bottom, and 90° right to left.

11 d Option b can be rejected because the dot is already visible. Cubes 1 and 2 show us the four squares are opposite the spiral, so option c can be ruled out. Cube 2 shows us the cross is to the left of the spiral if the dot is on the top, so option a can be ruled out. Cube 3 is cube 2 rotated 90° right to left.

12 b Options c and d can be rejected because 'B' and the square are already visible. Option a can be rejected because the circle is above the 'B'. Cube 3 is cube 1 rotated 90° anticlockwise in the plane of the page.

13 b Cube 1 shows the chevron is next to the 'W' shape. Cube 2 shows the chevron points to the diamond. So in cube 3, because the chevron is next the to 'W' shape, which is on the opposite side of the magnifying glass, it must point to the diamond.

14 b There should be a block of two cubes on the top back of the figure. This rules out options a, c and d.

15 d Options a and b are ruled out because the figure has two single cubes on the left side when rotated. Option c is ruled out because there is a 2-cube vertical block on the bottom right of the figure.

16 c Options a and b are ruled out because the original figure has a 2-cube block on the top row pointing backwards. Option d is ruled out because it should have a 2-cube block on the upper left side.

17 c Option a is ruled out because it is missing a cube at the back. Options b and d are ruled out because there should be a 2-cube vertical block in the centre.

Test 7
(pages 32–35)

1 c Options b and d are ruled out because the folded part of the figure should be visible, not cut off. Option a is ruled out because the fold is too high up: on two vertices of the triangle.

2 d Options a and c are ruled out because the folded part of the figure should be visible, not

cut off. Option b is ruled out because the fold is in the wrong place; it is not on the vertex of the triangular end.

3 c Options a and b are ruled out because the folded part of the figure should be visible, not cut off. Option d is ruled out because the fold is in the wrong place; it has been incorrectly folded at the top vertex of the triangular end.

4 a Option b is ruled out because the top, middle and bottom will be rectangles. Option c is ruled out because rows 2 and 4 will still be visible. Option d is ruled out because the top, middle and bottom will project to the left of rows 2 and 4.

5 b Options c and d are ruled out because the folded part of the figure should be visible, not cut off. Option a is ruled out because the fold is not on a diameter of the circle.

6 d Options a and c can be rejected because you need a 4-cube 'L' shape. You need three more cubes altogether, so option b can be rejected. The large 'L' shape is rotated 90° anticlockwise in the plane of the page with the cube on the left and the 2-cube shape at the back.

7 b You need seven cubes altogether, so options a, c and d can be rejected. Two 2-cube blocks make an 'L' shape, with the other in front and the single cube on the right.

8 d You need eight cubes altogether, so options a and b can be rejected. Option c can be ruled out because you don't need a 3-cube block. Two 2-cube blocks and single cubes are put together to make two 'i's. One is rotated 90° clockwise and the other is rotated through 180°. They are stuck together and the final 2-cube block is at the back.

9 b There is nowhere a 3-cube 'L' shape can fit, so options a and d can be rejected. There are no hidden cubes, so you need six cubes altogether. Option c can be ruled out. Two cubes are stacked on top of each other in the centre of the figure with a 2-cube block rotated 90° clockwise in the plane of the page at the back. Another 2-cube block sits to the top left of the figure.

10 d Option a is ruled out because the large face should not be shaded. Options b and c are ruled out because the large (non-curved) rectangular face should not be shaded.

11 b Options a and c are ruled out because there should be two shaded faces next to each other. Option d is ruled out because there should not be two white faces next to each other.

12 d Option b is ruled out because the large octagonal shape should not be shaded. Options a and c are ruled out because there should not be two shaded faces next to each other.

13 a Options b and d are ruled out because the rectangular face at the top of the 'F' shape should be shaded. Option c is ruled out because there should not be two shaded faces at the top of the 'F' shape.

14 b You need four cubes for the back layer and one for the front layer.

Option b fits onto the back right of the figure.

15 c You need five cubes for the back layer (one middle of left column, one bottom of middle column and three right column) and none for the front layer.

Option c fits onto the back of the figure.

16 b You need three cubes for the back layer and three for the front layer.

Option b fits onto the right and front of the figure.

17 a You need four cubes in an 'L' shape for the front layer and one or two for the left column of the front layer (depending on what's hidden). Options b and c don't fit.

Option a fits onto the front left of the figure.

Test 8

(pages 36–38, 59)

1 e Options a and f can be ruled out because they have double black blocks. Option e is the only other one with the required number of white blocks. Shape e has been rotated 180° from right to left.

2 c Options a and f can be ruled out because they have double black blocks. Option c is made from a 3-cube block, a 2-cube block and a single cube block. Shape c has been rotated 90° anticlockwise in the plane of the page, then rotated 90° towards you from top to bottom.

3 d Options a and f can be ruled out because they have double black blocks. Option d is the only remaining option with a white 2-cube block and four grey blocks. Shape d has been rotated 90° anticlockwise in the plane of the page.

4 a The answer must be options a or f because these have black blocks. Option a has a 2-cube black block next to a 3-cube grey block. Shape a has been rotated 90° anticlockwise in the plane of the page, then 90° clockwise from front to back.

5 f The answer must be options a or f because these have black blocks. Option f has a 3-cube black block. Shape f has been rotated 90° clockwise on its base, then tilted clockwise in the plane of the page.

6 b Options a and f can be ruled out because they have black blocks. Option b has a 2-cube grey block joined to a white cube, with a grey cube to its left. Shape b has been rotated 90° from right to left.

7 c
8 a
9 d
10 b
11 c

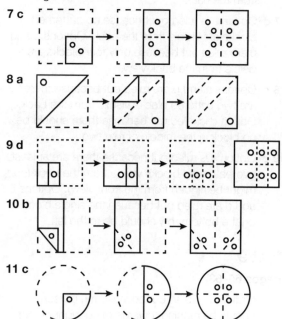

12 a Option b is ruled out because the tip of the ice cream shape should point to the sun. Option c is ruled out because the tail of the 'Q' should be pointing to the top right corner of the square (the corner diagonally opposite the one nearest the base of the ice cream). Option d is ruled out because the sun and 'Q' shapes should be next to each other, not on opposite sides as they are on the net.

13 d Option a is ruled out because the smiley face and arrow shape should be next to each other, not on opposite sides. Option b is ruled out because the bar should be pointing to the 'V' shape. Option c is ruled out because the 'V' shape should be the right way up when to the right of the smiley face.

14 a Option b is ruled out because the tick mark and diamond should be next to each other, not on opposite sides as they are on the net. Option c is ruled out because the circle should be next to the diamond, not on the opposite sides. Option d is ruled out because the circle should be above the tick, with the tick upright.

15 b Options a, c and d are ruled out because the arrow should point towards the circle.

16 a Options b and c are ruled out because only two patterned blocks are visible from the back. Option d is ruled out because the column of three blocks is on the right side when viewed from the back.

17 d Option a is ruled out because no patterned blocks are visible from the back. Options b and c are ruled out because only four blocks are visible from the back view.

18 c Options a and b are ruled out because there are two pattered blocks visible from the back. Option d is ruled out because there should be no block in the middle of row two.

19 c Option a is ruled out because there are at least two patterned blocks visible from the back (one might be hidden from the front view). Options b and d are ruled out because the single block on the bottom row should be to the left.

Test 9

(pages 60–63)

1 a Option b is ruled out because the person should be running towards the doughnut, not the arrow. Option c is ruled out because the spotted pattern must be opposite the running person. Option d is ruled out because the white arrow should point towards the side with the shaded and white triangles.

2 d Option a is ruled out because the triangles must have parallel sides next to each other. Option b is ruled out because the diagonal stripe and the white triangle must be on opposite sides.

Option c is ruled out because the diagonal stripe should point to the white part of the side that is half white and half shaded triangles.

3 c Option a is ruled out because the square and diagonal line with the dots should be on opposite sides, not next to each other. Option b is ruled out because the three dots should not be parallel to the star. Option d is ruled out because the star and shaded triangles should be on opposite sides, not next to each other.

4 d Options a and b are ruled out because the arrow should point towards the black square. Option c is ruled out because the flower and black square should be on opposite sides, not next to each other.

5 c Options a, b and d are ruled out because there should be a 2-cube block at the back.

6 b Options c and d are ruled out because there should be a 2-cube block at the back. Option a is ruled out because the 2-cube block on the front left should point to the left not forwards.

7 d They are all the right shape so you must look at individual blocks. Options a and b are ruled out because the vertical block should be three individual cubes. Option c is ruled out because there should be a 2-cube block at the end of the row on the right.

8 d Option a is ruled out because there is a missing cube to the left of the tallest column. Options b and c are ruled out because there should be an 'L'-shaped block in the middle of the figure.

9 b You need one cube for the back and all of the front layer. Option b fits onto the front left of the figure.

10 d You need two cubes for the back and three for the front layer. Option d fits onto the bottom front of the figure.

11 c You need four cubes for the back and one for the front layer. Option c has to be rotated 90° anticlockwise in the plane of the page and then it will fit onto the top back of the figure.

12 a You need four cubes for the back and two for the front layer. Option a has to be rotated 180° in the plane of the page and then it will fit onto the right side of the figure.

13 d Options b and c can be rejected because these faces are already visible. Option a can be rejected because from cube 1 we can see the 'P' should be to the right of the triangle. Cube 3 is cube 2 rotated 90° clockwise in the plane of the page.

14 c Option d can be rejected because the question mark is already visible. Option a can be ruled out because cube 1 shows us the circle is to the left of the question mark. Cubes 1 and 2 show us the two quarter-circles are opposite the question mark, so option b can be ruled out. Cube 3 is cube 2 rotated 90° towards you from top to bottom, then 90° clockwise in the plane of the page.

15 d Options a and b can be rejected because these faces are already visible. Option c can be ruled out because this would have to match cube 2. Cube 3 is cube 1 rotated 90° towards you from top to bottom.

16 a Option d can be rejected because this face is already visible. From the orientation of the semicircles on cube 2 we can see we need the face opposite the rocket, so options b and c can be ruled out. Cube 3 is cube 2 rotated 90° clockwise in the plane of the page.

Test 10
(pages 64–67)

1 b Options a and c are ruled out because the part of the figure above and below the fold line should be visible. Option d is ruled out because the fold is too high up.

2 d Options b and c are ruled out because the part of the figure above and below the fold line should be visible. Option a is ruled out because the fold is too low down.

3 d Options a and b are ruled out because the part of the figure to the left of the fold line should be visible. Option c is ruled out because the fold should be just below the apex of the triangle.

4 a Options b and d are ruled out because the part of the figure to the right and the left of the fold line should be visible. Option c is ruled out because the fold should be on the left arm of the 'Y', not just its stem.

5 b Option c is ruled out because we should only see a semicircle. Option a is ruled out because it doesn't show the cut-out sector. Option d is ruled out because one of the radii should be horizontal.

6 b Option a is ruled out because there is an extra block below the top patterned block. Options c and d are ruled out because there should be three blocks in the bottom row when viewed from the left.

7 b Options a and d are ruled out because there are only two patterned blocks visible from the left. Option c is ruled out because only two blocks will be visible in the right-hand column.

8 a Options c and d are ruled out because there are three patterned blocks visible when viewed from the left. Option b is ruled out because there should be no hole in the middle.

9 c Options a, b and d are ruled out because there should be a gap in the centre at the top.

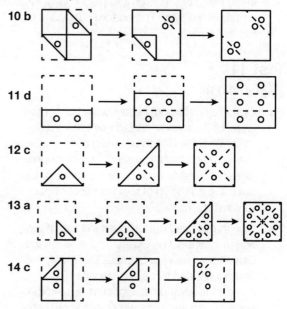

10 b

11 d

12 c

13 a

14 c

15 c Options a and b can be ruled out because you need an 'L' shape made of four cubes. Option d can be rejected because the remaining part is made of a double block and a single cube. The large 'L' shape is at the bottom of the figure, the cube is on top at the back with the 2-cube block at the top front of the figure.

16 b Option a can be ruled out because there is no 'L'-shaped block. You need seven cubes altogether, so options c and d can be rejected. A 2-cube block is rotated 90° clockwise in the plane of the page and placed at the back bottom of the figure. A cube is at the front bottom with the other 2-cube blocks on top.

17 a We cannot tell if there is a space or cube in the centre of this figure, so you need seven or eight cubes altogether; hence option b can be rejected. If the 'L' shape from option c were used (middle layer), the remainder would have to be separate cubes, so option c can be ruled out. If the 'T' shape from option d were used, we would need two more single cubes; hence option d can be ruled out. The 'T' shape is rotated 90° anticlockwise in the plane of the page with a cube placed to the bottom. Another cube is to the right of the 'T' shape and the 2-cube block to the left.

18 d Three double blocks and a single cube are required, so options a, b and c can be rejected. Two 2-cube blocks are rotated 90° clockwise in the plane of the page and placed behind and on top of the third. The bottom right cube is at the bottom left.

Test 11

(pages 68–71)

1 c Option a is ruled out because the tip, not the base, of the triangle should point towards the three lines. Option b is ruled out because the heart and half circle should be on opposite sides, not next to each other. Option d is ruled out because the tip of the heart should point towards the circle.

2 a Option b is ruled out because the top of the tick mark should be closest to the 'S' shape. Option c is ruled out because the wiggly line and square should be on opposite sides, not next to each other. Option d is ruled out because the arrow should point towards the tick mark.

3 c Option a is ruled out because the flower and question mark should be on opposite sides. Option b is ruled out because the striped circle and smiley face should be on opposite sides, not next to each other. Option d is ruled out because the bottom of the question mark should be nearest the linked circles, not the square.

4 b Option a is ruled out because the clock and oval shapes should be on opposite sides, not next to each other. Option c is ruled out because the longer oval axis should be parallel to the 'X' shape. Option d is ruled out because

the cross and the 'X' shape should be on opposite sides.

5 d You need a black, a white and a grey 2-cube block, so it must be option d. Shape d has been rotated 90° clockwise from front to back.

6 b Options a and f can be ruled out because they do not have black blocks (although one could be hidden in this view of option a). You need a single black cube, so options c and d can be ruled out. Option e can be ruled out because it only has one white block. Shape b has been rotated 90° right to left.

7 f Options a and f are the only ones with no black blocks (although one could be hidden in this view of option a). Option a can be ruled out because it does not have a 3-cube block. Shape f has been rotated 90° towards from you from top to bottom.

8 e Options b and e are very similar but option b has a single cube and a double block on the bottom, while option e has a 3-cube block. Shape e has been rotated 90° anticlockwise on its base.

9 a Options a and f are the only ones with no black blocks (although one could be hidden in this view of option a). Option f can be ruled out because it has two 3-cube blocks. Shape a has been rotated 90° anticlockwise in the plane of the page, and away from you from top to bottom.

10 c You need two 2-cube grey blocks, one white 3-cube 'L' shape and one black 2-cube block. Shape c has been rotated 90° away from you from top to bottom.

11 b Options a and c are ruled out because the large rectangular faces should be shaded. Option d is ruled out because the front diamond-shaped face should be shaded.

12 c Option b is ruled out because the 'L' shape is not shaded. Option a is ruled out because the left-hand face is not shaded. Option d is ruled out because the top square face should be shaded.

13 b Option a is ruled out because the 'T' shape should not be shaded. Option c is ruled out because the rectangular face at the top of the 'T' should be shaded. Option d can be ruled out because two shaded faces should not be next to each other.

14 a Options b and c are ruled out because two shaded faces should not be next to each other. Option d is ruled out because the triangular faces should alternate in colour.

15 d Option b is ruled out because the cross with arrows is diagonal, not perpendicular to the edges. Option c is ruled out because the 'T' shape should be next to the '7'. Option a is ruled out because the arrows should point to the right-hand side of the '7', not the top of it.

16 b Option a is ruled out because the bottom (tip) of the heart should not point to the hash mark. Option c is ruled out because the hash mark and heart should be next to each other. Option d is ruled out because the top of the heart, not the tip, should be closest to the clock.

17 a Option b is ruled out because the tip of the pencil shape should point towards the half circle. Option c is ruled out because the flat side of the half circle should be facing the letter 'A'. Option d is ruled out because the pencil shape and letter 'A' should be next to each other.

18 c Option a is ruled out because the cross with arrows and the horizontal lines should be next to each other, not on opposite sides. Options b and d are ruled out because the top, not the bottom, of the ice cream cone should be nearest the cross with arrows.

Test 12
(pages 72–75)

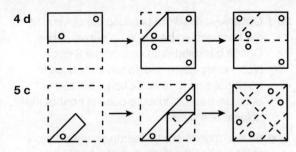

1 a

2 b

3 d

4 d

5 c

6 c The triangle points towards the point of the arrow, so it is option c. Cube 3 is cube 1 rotated 90° anticlockwise in the plane of the page, then 90° anticlockwise on its base.

7 a Option c can be rejected because it is already visible. Cube 2 shows us option a is to the left of the upright 'Y' and to the right of the triangle and square when the triangle and square is at the top. This matches with cube 3. Cube 3 is cube 2 rotated 90° left to right and then 90° towards you from top to bottom.

8 d Option b can be rejected because it is already visible. Cube 2 shows us option d is to the right of the upright 'TV on a stand' shape and points to the parallel lines going lengthways. This matches with cube 3. Cube 3 is cube 2 rotated 90° towards you from top to bottom, and 90° anticlockwise in the plane of the page.

9 b Cubes 1 and 2 show we have the choice of options c, a and b. Cube 1 shows that the shape to the right of 'Concorde' (when pointing upwards) is the hidden left side of cube 3. So, we need the shape opposite the half-shaded square. Option c can be ruled out. Cube 3 is cube 2 rotated 90° towards you from top to bottom.

10 c All the options are the same shape so you must look at the individual blocks. Options a, b and d are ruled out because they do not have a 2-cube block in the middle running bottom front to back.

11 a Option b is ruled out because it has an extra cube to the bottom left of the figure. Option c is ruled out because it has a 2-cube block on the bottom. Option d is ruled out because the vertical 2-cube block is at the top not on the bottom of the stack.

12 d Option a is ruled out because the column at the back should be made up of two cubes. Option b is ruled out because the 2-cube block laying down should run from back to front, not side to side. Option c is ruled out because there is an extra cube in front of the column at the back.

13 d All the options are the same shape so you must look at the individual blocks. Option a is ruled out because there should be a vertical 2-cube block on the right at the back of the figure. Options b and c are ruled out because there should be a 2-cube block at the bottom front pointing backwards.

14 a Option b is ruled out because the arrow should point towards the circle, not away from it. Option c is ruled out because the arrow should point away from the top of the 'T' shape. Option d is ruled out because the circle and the 'T' shape should be on opposite sides.

15 b Option a is ruled out because number '8' and the triangle should be on opposite sides, not next to each other. Option c is ruled out because the shaded part of the circle should be nearest the sun. Option d is ruled out because the tip (apex), not the base, of the triangle should point towards the hash mark.

16 d Option a is ruled out because the heart and the striped square should be on opposite sides, not next to each other. Option b is ruled out because the arrow should point towards the number '2', not away from it. Option c is ruled out because the stripes in the square should point from top left to bottom right.

17 c Option a is ruled out because the bottom, not the top, of the exclamation mark should be nearest the ladder shape. Option b is ruled out because the open part of the half-moon should point towards the square with the cross inside. Option d is ruled out because the half-moon and exclamation mark should be on opposite sides, not next to each other.

Test 13
(pages 76–79)

1 b You need six cubes altogether, so options c and d can be rejected. Option a can be ruled out because it does not have two 2-cube blocks. Two 2-cube blocks are to the left of the figure, with a cube on top and a cube in the front.

2 a You need seven cubes altogether, so options b, c and d can be rejected. A 2-cube block is placed vertically, back left, and another vertically back right. Another 2-cube block protrudes forward and a cube is to the right.

3 d You need one 3-cube 'L' shape, so options a and c can be ruled out. You also need one single cube, so option b can be rejected. The 'L' shape is at the bottom left with the 2-cube blocks vertical at the back left and right.

4 c You need seven cubes altogether, so options a, b and d can be rejected. The 'L' shape is on top of the cubes to the right of the figure with the 2-cube block vertical at the back left of the figure.

5 c Options a, b and d are ruled out because the long side face should be shaded.

6 b Option a is ruled out because the top rectangular face facing us should be shaded. Option c is ruled out because the large rectangular face should not be shaded. Option d is ruled out because the trapezoidal face should be shaded.

7 c Options a and d are ruled out because there should not be more than two shaded faces. Option b is ruled out because the bottom should not be shaded.

8 a Option b is ruled out because the face of the hexagon shape should be shaded. Option c is ruled out because the lower sloping rectangular face should not be shaded. Option d is ruled out because there should not be two shaded rectangular faces next to each other.

9 c You need one cube for the back layer and all of the front layer. Option c fits onto the front of the figure.

10 a You need one cube for the back layer and two horizontal cubes for the front layer. Option a slides onto the front right of the figure.

11 d You need four cubes for the back layer. Option d has to be rotated 90° towards you from top to bottom. It is then rotated 90° from right to left. It now fits at the back right side of the figure.

12 b You need two horizontal cubes for the middle of the back layer, and possibly some for the bottom row, depending on what is hidden. You also need three vertical cubes for the left side of the front layer. Options a and c can be rejected. Option d can be rejected because it only has one cube in the back middle row (when rotated 90° clockwise in the plane of the page). Option b has to be rotated 90° clockwise in the plane of the page. It will then fit onto the left of the figure.

13 e Shapes c, d and f can be ruled out because they have black blocks. You want a skinny 'S' shape with an extra bit on one side. Shape e has been rotated 90° towards you from top to bottom, then 90° clockwise in the plane of the page.

14 b You need a grey and a white 2-cube block stacked on top of each other. Shape b has been rotated 90° from right to left.

15 f You need a black block with a grey and a white 2-cube block on two sides. Shape f has been rotated 90° away from you from bottom to top.

16 a You need a grey and a white 2-cube block at right angles with a single white cube on the end of the grey block. Shapes c, d and f can be ruled out because they have black blocks. Shape a has been rotated 90° from left to right.

17 d You need a grey column with a black cube at one end, and white and grey blocks at the other. Shape d has been rotated 90° clockwise in the plane of the page.

18 c You need a shape with at least two black blocks. Shape c has been rotated 180° on its base, then 90° away from you from bottom to top.

Test 14

(pages 80–83)

1 c Options b and d are ruled out because the folded part cannot be seen. Option a is rejected because the back part is too small.

2 b Option d is ruled out because the part of the figure above the fold line should be visible. Option a is ruled out because the fold is too high. Option c is ruled out because the fold is too low, on the vertices of the shape.

3 c Option b is ruled out because the part of the figure to the left of the fold line should be visible. Option d is ruled out because the fold isn't on the diameter of the circle. Option a is ruled out because the fold is too far to the left.

4 c Options b and d are ruled out because the part of the figure to the left of the fold line should be visible. Option a is ruled out because the fold is too far to the right.

5 a Options b and d are ruled out because the folded parts are the wrong shape. Option c is ruled out because the part of the figure above the fold line should be visible.

6 b Option a is ruled out because the rectangle should be in line with the chevrons. Option c is ruled out because the chevrons run in the wrong direction. Option d is ruled out because the rectangle and arrows should be next to each other, not on opposite sides.

7 a Options b and c are ruled out because the shaded part of the square should face the fork shape. Option d is ruled out because the fork should be next to the sun.

8 a Options b and d are ruled out because the axis of the linked circles should be in line with the base of the triangle. Option c is ruled out because the triangle should point at the apex of the three dots.

9 d Options a and b are ruled out because the tip of the tear drop shape should be pointing to the base of the pine tree shape. Option c is ruled out because the pine tree shape and the 'T' shape should be next to each other, not on opposite sides.

10 b Options a and d are ruled out because there are two patterned blocks visible from above. Option c is ruled out because only four blocks are visible from above.

11 c There is only one patterned block visible from above, which rules out options a and d. Option b is ruled out because six blocks are visible from above.

12 a Options b and c are ruled out because there are two patterned blocks visible from above. Option d is ruled out because six blocks are visible from above.

13 d Options a and c are ruled out because there are two patterned blocks visible from above.

Option b is ruled out because seven blocks are visible from above.

14 d Options b and c can be rejected because these faces are already visible. Cubes 1 and 3 show us we want the face opposite the pointed oval. Option a can be ruled out because this is next to the pointed oval. Cube 3 is cube 1 rotated 90° anticlockwise in the plane of the page.

15 b Option a is ruled out because this face is already visible. Cubes 1 and 3 show us the ice cream is opposite the arrow, so option d can be rejected. Cubes 2 and 3 show us we want the face opposite the oval, so option c can be rejected. Cube 3 is cube 1 rotated 180° on its base.

16 c Cube 2 shows us the 'i' shape is to the right of the smiley face, so it must be option a or c. The dot of the 'i' and the eyes of the smiley face are in line, so it must be option c. Cube 3 is cube 2 rotated 90° left to right then 90° towards you from top to bottom.

17 c Cubes 1 and 2 show us 'A' and 'V' are on opposite sides, so it must be option a or c. Cube 2 shows 'V' is to the right of 'T' and turned through 90° with the open end towards the 'T'. The face we want is to the right of 'T', if 'T' were the right way up, so it is option c. Cube 3 is cube 2 rotated 90° right to left, then rotated 90° clockwise in the plane of the page.

Test 15

(pages 84–87)

1 b You need five cubes altogether, so options c and d can be ruled out. A 2-cube block is rotated 90° clockwise in the plane of the page and is at the back of the figure. A second 2-cube block is to the top right and the single cube is on the bottom left.

2 d You need a 'T' shape, so option b can be rejected. There is nowhere to fit a 3-cube 'L' shape, so option a can be ruled out. The 'T' shape is rotated 180° in the plane of the page. To the left of the 'T' shape are two cubes stacked on top of each other and a 2-cube block is at the back.

3 a You need three 2-cube blocks, so options b, c and d can be ruled out. The three 2-cube

blocks are arranged as in the figure with the single cube at the bottom back of the figure.

4 c You need a 'T' shape, so option b can be rejected. You need nine or ten cubes altogether (depending on what is hidden), so option a can be ruled out. There is nowhere for a 3-cube block to fit, so option d can be rejected. The 'T' shape is rotated 90° anticlockwise in the plane of the page. To the left of the 'T' shape is a 2-cube block. On top of the 'T' shape is a cube and to the bottom back of the figure is a 2-cube block.

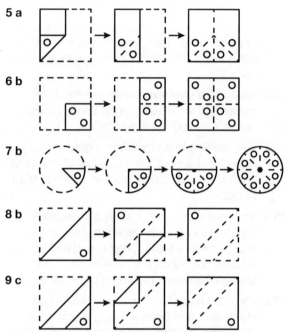

5 a

6 b

7 b

8 b

9 c

10 e You want an 'n' shape that includes two grey cubes and a black block. Shape e has been rotated 90° right to left, then 90° towards you from top to bottom.

11 d You need a square with two diagonal black cubes and two diagonal grey cubes, so it must be option d. Shape d has been rotated 90° away from you from bottom to top.

12 f You need six grey and white cubes altogether. Shape f has been rotated 90° away you from top to bottom.

13 c You need a black 2-cube block and a grey 2-cube block, so it must be option c or e. Shape e has an extra white cube, so it must be option c. Shape c has been rotated 180° right to left.

14 a This is a shape with three alternating grey and white cubes in a row. Shape a has been rotated 180° in the plane of the page.

15 b You need a square with two diagonal black cubes, a grey and a white cube, so it must be option b. Shape b has been rotated 180° from right to left.

16 c Option a is ruled out because there should be a 2-cube block at the bottom left of the figure. Options b and d are ruled out because there should not be three cubes at the base of the figure.

17 b All the figures are the same shape, so you must look at the individual blocks. Options a, c and d are ruled out because they only have one 2-cube block.

18 d Option a is ruled out because the 2-cube block at the bottom left of the figure should not run from left to right. Options b and c are ruled out because they only have one 2-cube block on the base of the figure.

19 c All the figures are the same shape, so you must look at the individual blocks. Options a and b are ruled out, because the 2-cube block on top of the column should be on the left with the single cube on the right. Option d is also ruled out because the bottom right of the figure should be made up of two 2-cube blocks.

PUZZLE ANSWERS

Puzzle 1

(page 88)

Practice makes perfect!

 = 5

5 has been rotated 180° front to back.

 = 2

2 has been rotated 180° in the plane of the page.

 = 4

4 has been rotated 90° clockwise in the plane of the page and 180° front to back.

 = 1

1 has been rotated 90° clockwise in the plane of the page and 180° on its base.

 = 3

3 has been rotated 90° front to back.

Building time

The top view shows it is an 'L' shape from a 2 × 2 square.

2 black, 1 grey and 1 white can be seen from the back. The grey and the white are the ones in the top view, so the top view has been rotated.

The back and side views show the shape is not more than two blocks high and two blocks wide. There are only black blocks on the bottom layer. As it is an 'L' shape there must be three of these.

If the black block in the top view was on the top layer we would see a black block in the top layer of the side or back views. So, there are no black blocks on the top layer. The white and grey blocks must be on the top layer. There are five blocks altogether.

White blocks = 1

Grey blocks = 1

Black blocks = 3

Puzzle 2

(page 89)

A riddle

Cube 1: F and B can be rejected because these are opposite E and J. The letters next to E and J are D and I, but I is to the right of these two letters so it must be **D**.

Cube 2: J and I can be rejected because these are opposite D and B. The letters next to D and B are E and F, but F is to the right of these two letters so it must be **E**.

Cube 3: E and I can be rejected because these are opposite D and F. The letters next to D and F are B and J, but J is to the right of these two letters so it must be **B**.

When the letters are unscrambled, the answer to the riddle is a bed.

Shape Sudoku

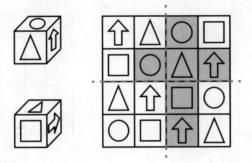

Puzzle 3
(page 90)
Yes, Chef!

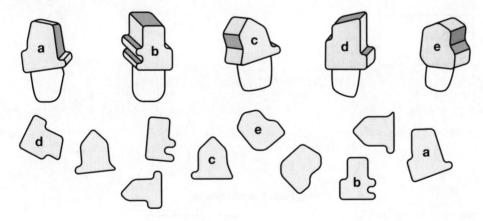

Odd one out

If cubes 1 and 3 matched, they would both have a leaf or a sun on the right-hand side.

If cubes 2 and 3 matched, they would both have the branch of leaves or a sun to the left of the cross of petals and the sun.

Cube 3 does not match with cube 1 or cube 2.

Cubes 1 and 2 match if the two different leaf patterns are on opposite sides.

Cube 3 is the odd one out.

Box 1

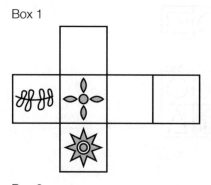

Box 3

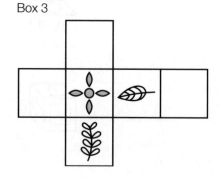

Box 2

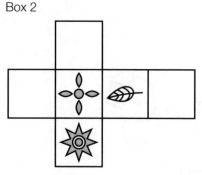

Puzzle 4

(page 91)

Hide and seek

You need a shape with one cube in the front layer, bottom right, so options b and e can be ruled out.

You need a shape with two cubes in the back layer, on the left, so option d can be ruled out.

You need a shape with one more cube in the back layer, centre top, so option a can be ruled out.

It must be option c.

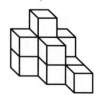

Paper decorations

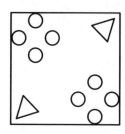

Puzzle 5

(page 92)

Origami

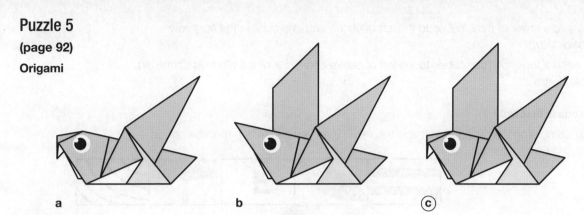

a b c

Puzzle 6

(page 93)

The creature

The creature is made from parts b, d, e, f and h.

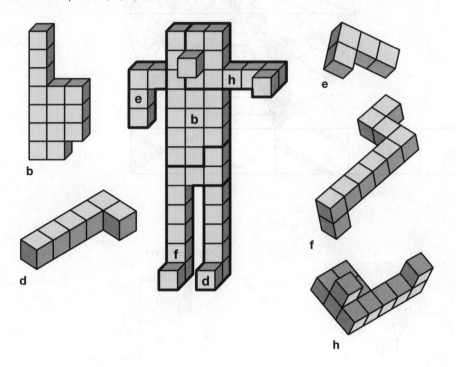

Puzzle 7

(page 94)

Special delivery

a: You need two cubes on three cubes in a middle layer of three.
a = 4 left side view

b: You need a tower of three cubes in the centre.
b = 5 left side view

c: You need a tower of three cubes to the left of centre and everything else on the bottom layer.
c = 2 right side view

d: You need a tower of three cubes to the left of centre and one cube in the front row.
d = 3 back view

e: You need a tower of three cubes to the left of centre and a row of three cubes on the left.
e = 1 back view

The circus is in town!

Start by completing the decagon from the top view. Then you can match the side panels.

Puzzle 8

(page 95)

Paper lantern

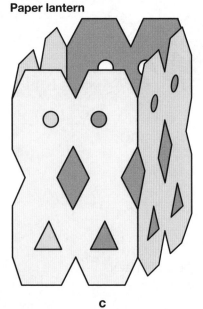

c

Number time

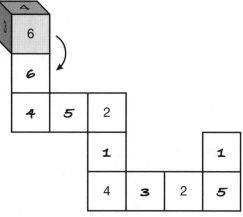

Test 8 continued from page 38

Which option shows a 2D view of the 3D figure from the *back*?

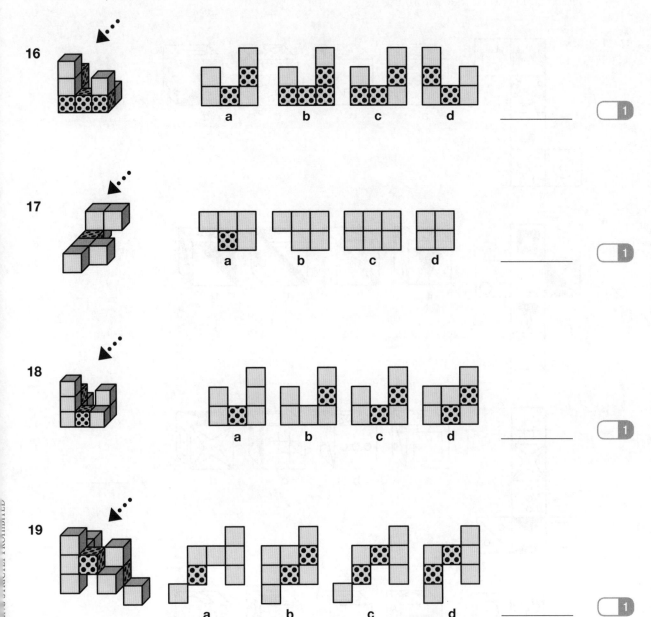

16   **a**   **b**   **c**   **d**   _____   1

17   **a**   **b**   **c**   **d**   _____   1

18   **a**   **b**   **c**   **d**   _____   1

19   **a**   **b**   **c**   **d**   _____   1

Total   19

Test 9

Which cube can be made from the net?

1

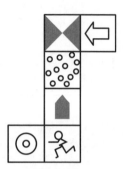

a   b   c   d   _____   1

2

a   b   c   d   _____   1

3

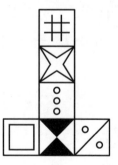

a   b   c   d   _____   1

4

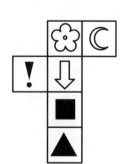

a   b   c   d   _____   1

Which option shows the 3D figure in the grey box viewed from the *right*?

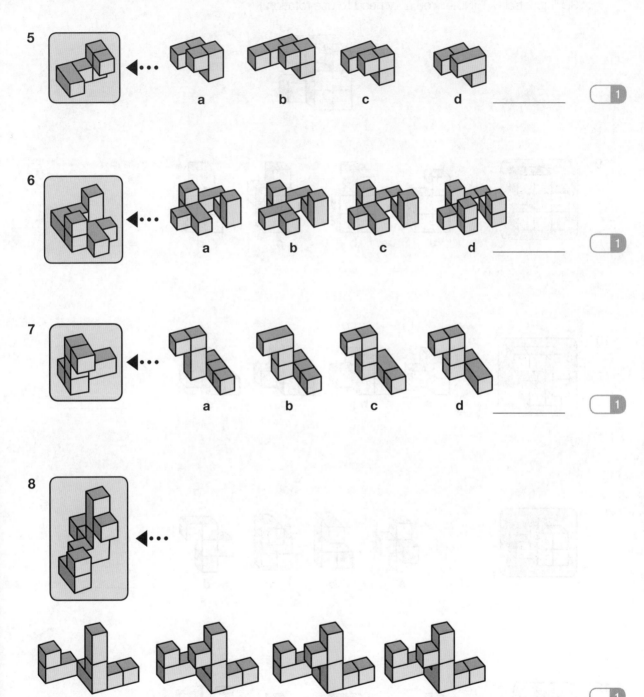

5

a b c d _____ 1

6

a b c d _____ 1

7

a b c d _____ 1

8

a b c d _____ 1

Which option can be added to the blocks in the grey box to create an exact copy of the 3D figure below? (Note: You may need to use rotation.)

9

                    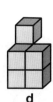

                       a   b   c   d _____ (1)

10

     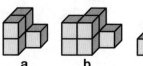   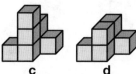

                       a   b   c   d _____ (1)

11

     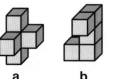   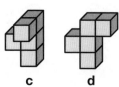

                       a   b   c   d _____ (1)

12

     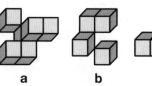   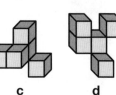

                       a   b   c   d _____ (1)

The figures in the grey box are three views of the same cube. Which option should replace the *blank* cube face?

13

a   b   c   d _____   1

14

a   b   c   d _____   1

15

a   b   c   d _____   1

16

a   b   c   d _____   1

Total   16

Test 10

Which option shows the figure in the grey box when folded along the dotted line?

1

a   b   c   d _____   ☐ 1

2

a   b   c   d _____   ☐ 1

3

a   b   c   d _____   ☐ 1

4

a   b   c   d _____   ☐ 1

5

a   b   c   d _____   ☐ 1

Which option shows a 2D view of the 3D figure from the *left*?

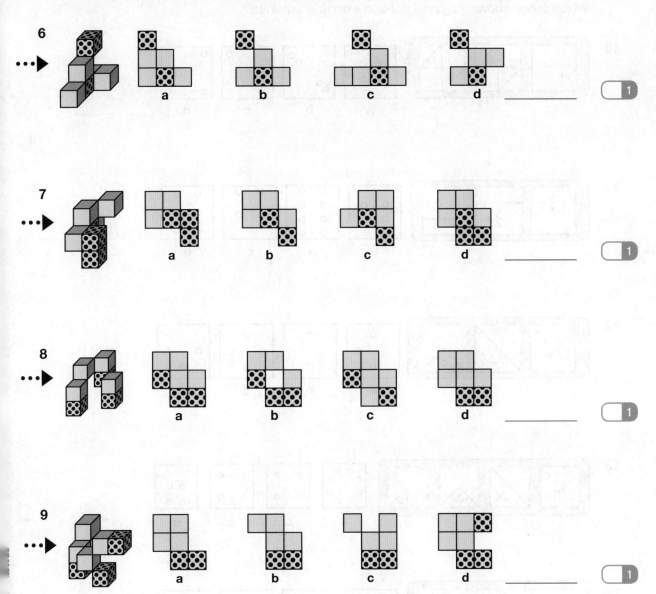

6
...▶
a   b   c   d _____   1

7
...▶
a   b   c   d _____   1

8
...▶
a   b   c   d _____   1

9
...▶
a   b   c   d _____   1

A shape is folded and then one or more holes is punched, as shown in the grey box.
Which option shows the correct shape when it is unfolded?

10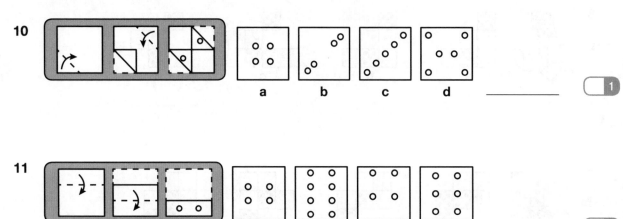

a   b   c   d _____ 1

11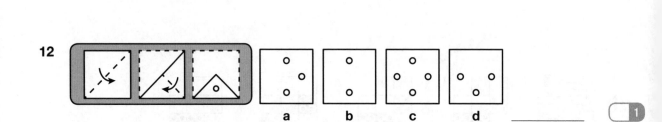

a   b   c   d _____ 1

12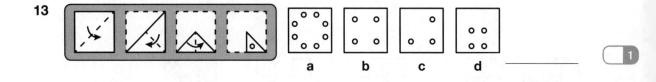

a   b   c   d _____ 1

13

a   b   c   d _____ 1

14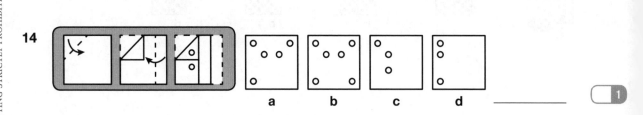

a   b   c   d _____ 1

Which set of blocks can be put together to make the 3D figure on the left?

15

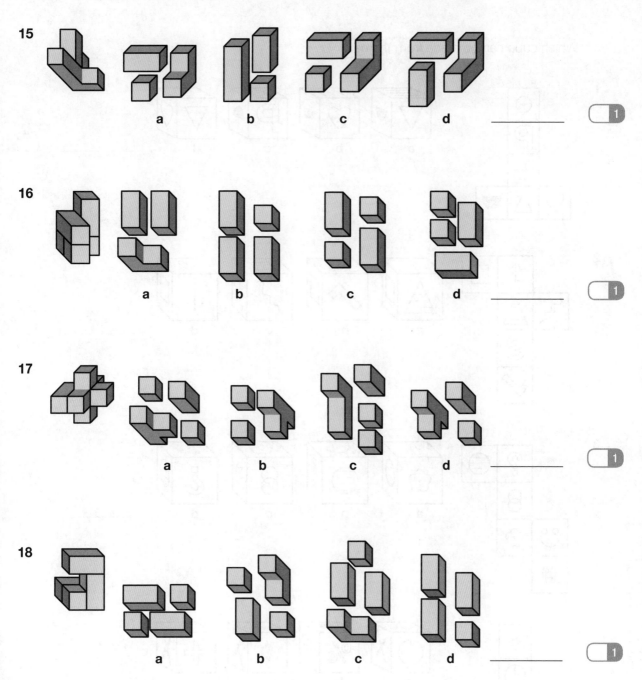

a   b   c   d   _____   1

16

a   b   c   d   _____   1

17

a   b   c   d   _____   1

18

a   b   c   d   _____   1

Total   18

Test 11

Which cube can be made from the net?

1

 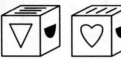 

a   b   c   d

_____ 1

2

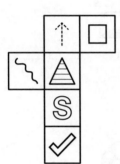

a   b   c   d

_____ 1

3

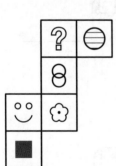

a   b   c   d

_____ 1

4

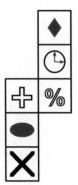

a   b   c   d

_____ 1

Which of the 3D figures in the grey box has been **rotated** to make the new 3D figure?

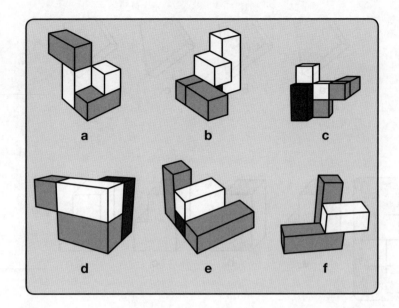

a   b   c

d   e   f

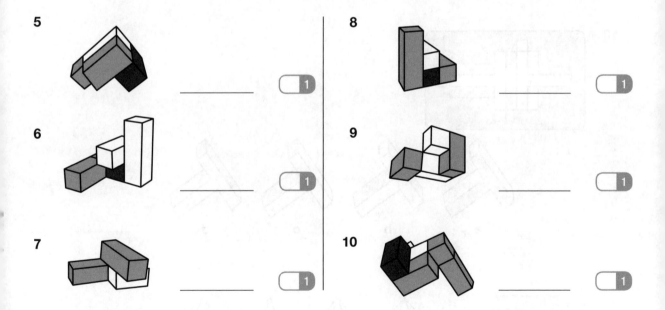

5 _____ (1)

6 _____ (1)

7 _____ (1)

8 _____ (1)

9 _____ (1)

10 _____ (1)

Which of the 3D shapes can be made from the shaded net in the grey box?

11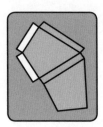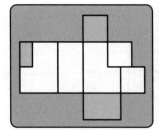

    a   **b**   **c**   **d** _____ ⬭1

12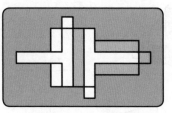

    a   **b**   **c**   **d** _____ ⬭1

13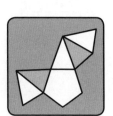

    a   **b**   **c**   **d** _____ ⬭1

14

    a   **b**   **c**   **d** _____ ⬭1

Which of the partial nets can be folded to make the cube shown?

15

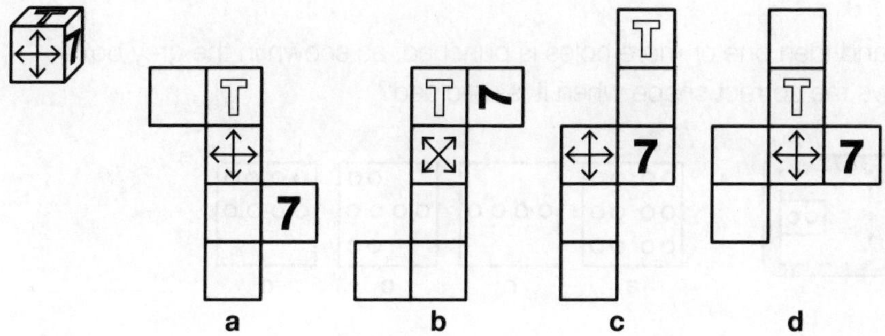

a   b   c   d

1

16

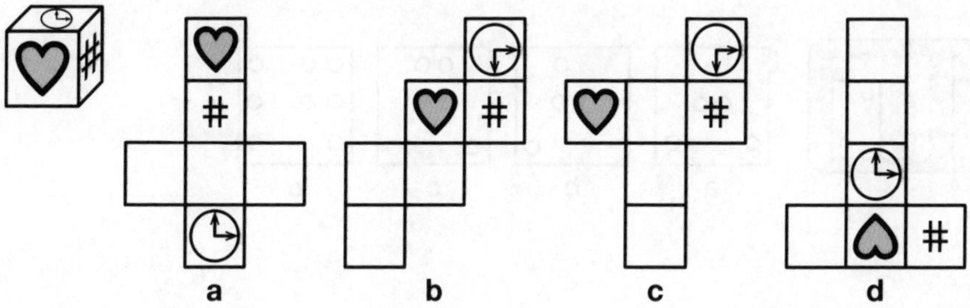

a   b   c   d

1

17

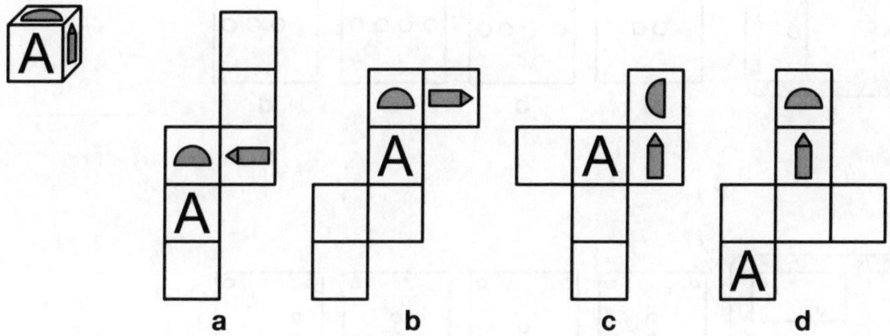

a   b   c   d

1

18

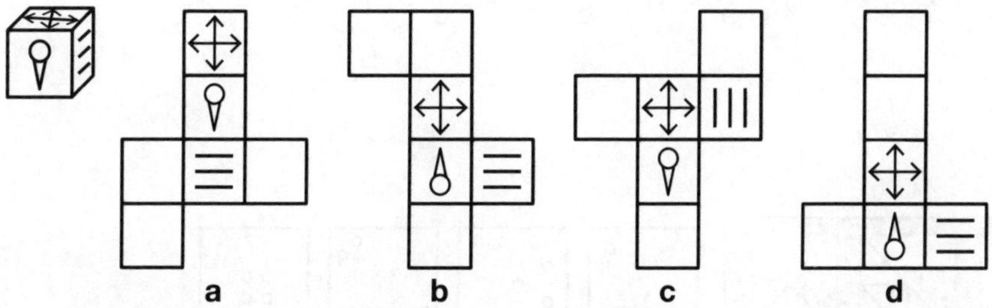

a   b   c   d

1

Test 12

A shape is folded and then one or more holes is punched, as shown in the grey box.
Which option shows the correct shape when it is unfolded?

1
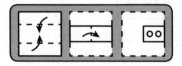

    a   b   c   d

_____ ⬜ 1

2
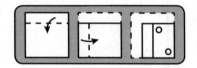

    a   b   c   d

_____ ⬜ 1

3
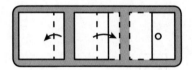
 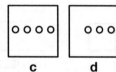

    a   b   c   d

_____ ⬜ 1

4
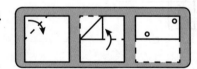

    a   b   c   d

_____ ⬜ 1

5
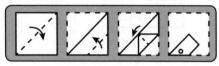

    a   b   c   d

_____ ⬜ 1

The figures in the grey box are three views of the same cube. Which option should replace the *blank* cube face?

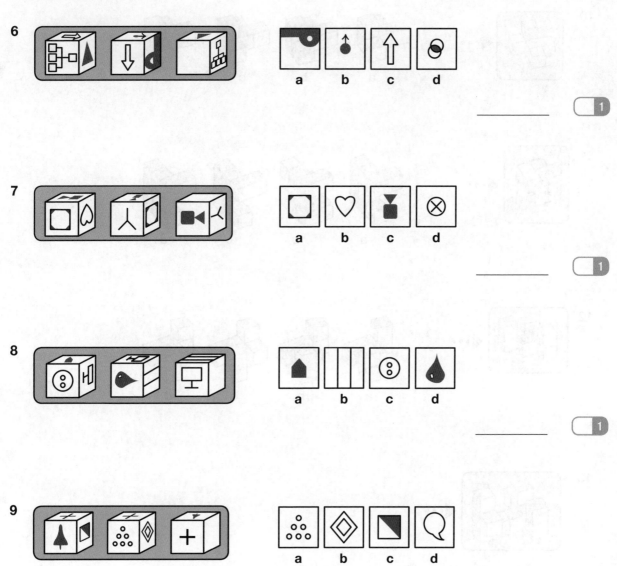

6

a b c d

_____ ◯1

7

a b c d

_____ ◯1

8

a b c d

_____ ◯1

9

a b c d

_____ ◯1

Which option shows the 3D figure in the grey box viewed from the *right*?

10

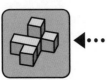 ◄•••

   a   **b**   **c**   **d**   _____

11

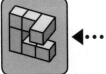 ◄•••

   a   **b**   **c**   **d**   _____

12

 ◄•••

   a   **b**   **c**   **d**   _____

13

 ◄•••

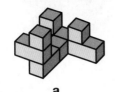 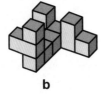 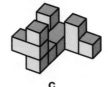 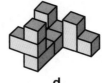
   a   **b**   **c**   **d**   _____

Which cube can be made from the net?

14

a   b   c   d

_____   1

15

a   b   c   d

_____   1

16

a   b   c   d

_____   1

17

a   b   c   d

_____   1

Total   17

Test 13

Which set of blocks can be put together to make the 3D figure on the left?

1

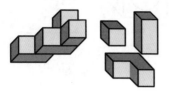 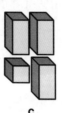

            a   b   c   d

   ⬚ 1

2

       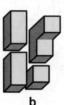

            a   b   c   d

   ⬚ 1

3

            a   b   c   d

   ⬚ 1

4

       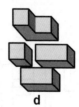

            a   b   c   d

   ⬚ 1

Which of the 3D shapes can be made from the shaded net in the grey box?

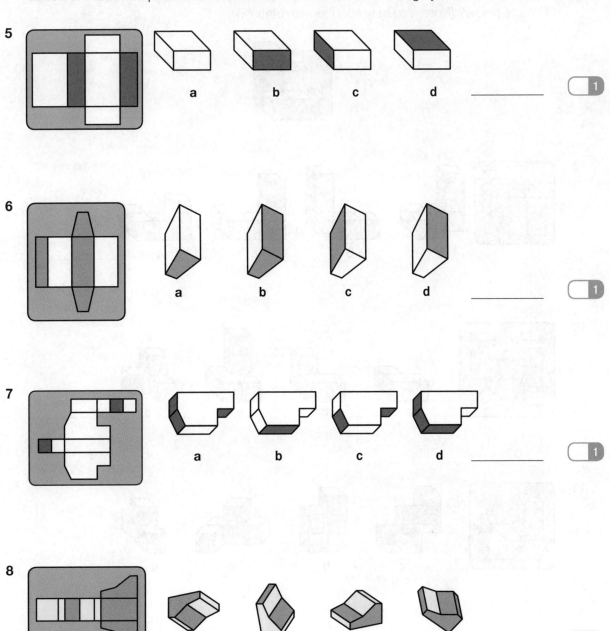

5   a   b   c   d   _____   1

6   a   b   c   d   _____   1

7   a   b   c   d   _____   1

8   a   b   c   d   _____   1

Which option can be added to the blocks in the grey box to create an exact copy of the 3D figure below? (Note: You may need to use rotation.)

9

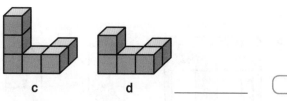

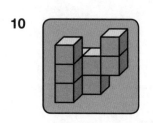   a   b   c   d   _____

10

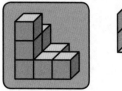   a   b   c   d   _____

11

a   b   c   d   _____

12

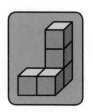   a   b   c   d   _____

Which of the 3D figures in the grey box has been **rotated** to make the new 3D figure?

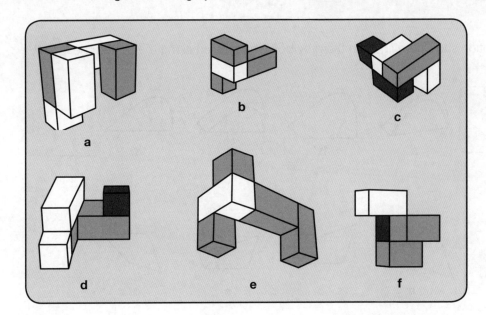

a

b

c

d

e

f

13 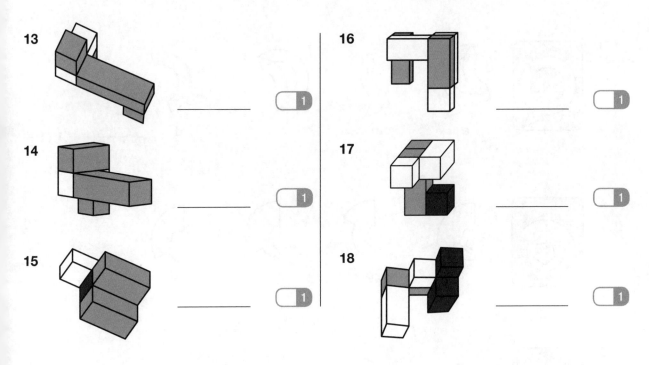 _____ ⬭1

14 _____ ⬭1

15 _____ ⬭1

16 _____ ⬭1

17 _____ ⬭1

18 _____ ⬭1

Total 18

Test 14

Which option shows the figure in the grey box when folded along the dotted line?

1

          a   b   c   d _____ 1

2

          a   b   c   d _____ 1

3

          a   b   c   d _____ 1

4

          a   b   c   d _____ 1

5

          a   b   c   d _____ 1

Which of the partial nets can be folded to make the cube shown?

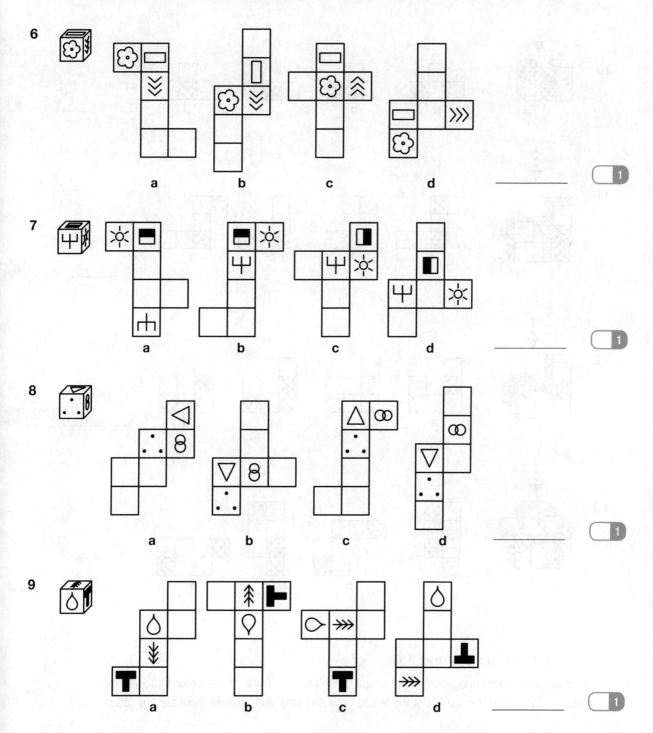

6

a   b   c   d

7

a   b   c   d

8

a   b   c   d

9

a   b   c   d

Which option shows a 2D view of the 3D figure from *above*?

10

a   b   c   d   _____

11

a   b   c   d   _____

12

a   b   c   d   _____

13

a   b   c   d   _____

2D Views of 3D Shapes from Above Tip!

With these questions, the height of the shape doesn't matter. Think of it as being flattened. You only need to look at the number of the blocks *wide* and *long*, and whether there are any gaps.

The figures in the grey box are three views of the same cube. Which option should replace the *blank* cube face?

14

a   b   c   d   _____   ⬭ 1

15

a   b   c   d   _____   ⬭ 1

16

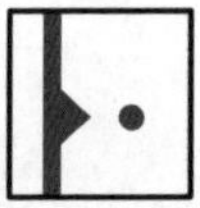

a   b   c   d   _____   ⬭ 1

17

a   b   c   d   _____   ⬭ 1

Total   17

Which set of blocks can be put together to make the 3D figure on the left?

1

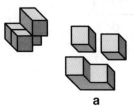 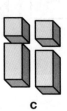 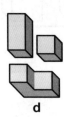

a   b   c   d _____ ①

2

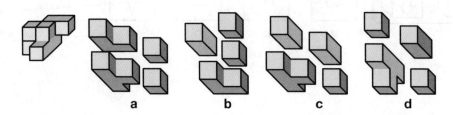

a   b   c   d _____ ①

3

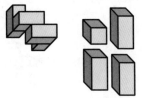 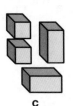

a   b   c   d _____ ①

4

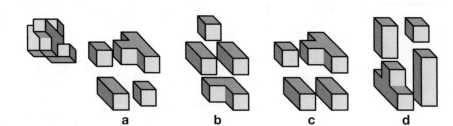

a   b   c   d _____ ①

A shape is folded and then one or more holes is punched, as shown in the grey box.
Which option shows the correct shape when it is unfolded?

5

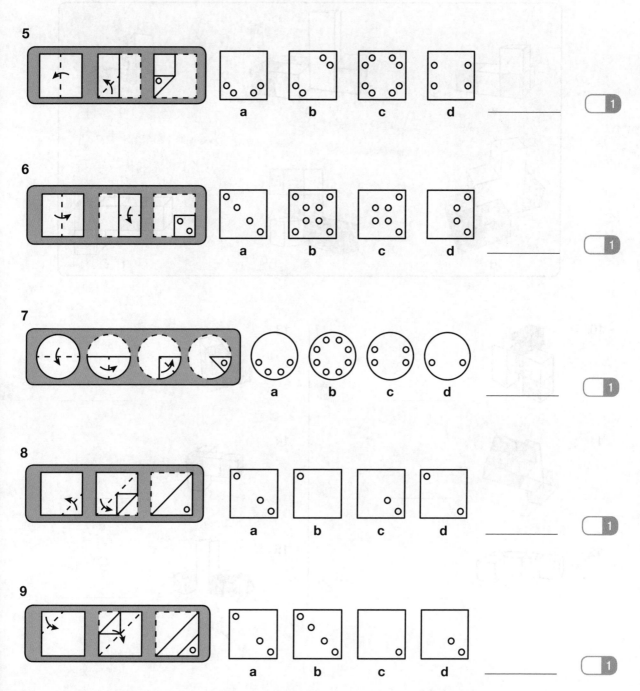

a   b   c   d

1

6

a   b   c   d

1

7

a   b   c   d

1

8

a   b   c   d

1

9

a   b   c   d

1

Which of the 3D figures in the grey box has been **rotated** to make the new 3D figure?

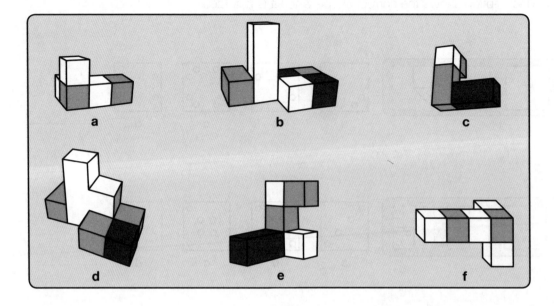

10 _____ (1)

11 _____ (1)

12 _____ (1)

13 _____ (1)

14 _____ (1)

15 _____ (1)

Which option shows the 3D figure in the grey box viewed from the *back*?

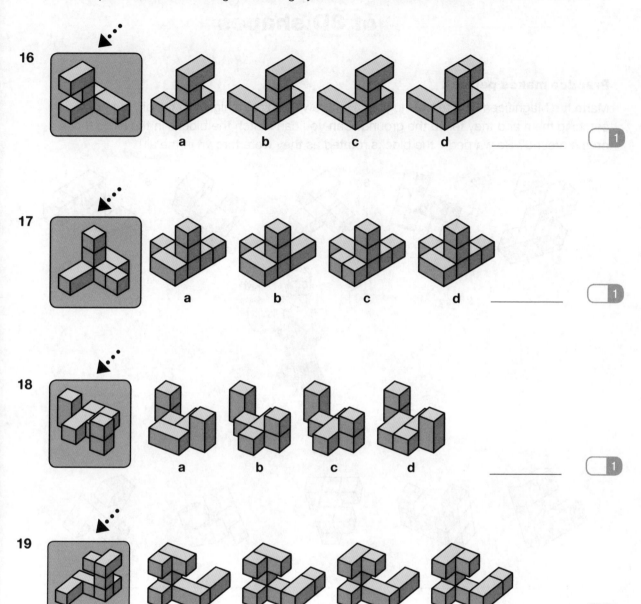

16   a   b   c   d   1

17   a   b   c   d   1

18   a   b   c   d   1

19   a   b   c   d   1

Total   19

Puzzle 1 — 3D rotation and 2D views of 3D shapes

Practice makes perfect!

Mario the Magnificent is a terrible juggler. He threw the blocks high into the air, but missed catching them and they fell to the ground. Can you can match the blocks in the air to those on the ground? Be warned – the blocks rotated as they were thrown in the air!

1   2   3   4   5

_____   _____   _____   _____   _____

Building time

Here are three views of a 3D figure made from cube-shaped blocks. If you were to build the figure, how many cubes of each colour would you need?

top   back   left side

white _____   grey _____   black _____

Puzzle 2 Nets and cubes (and Sudoku)

A riddle

Below are three views of the same cube, and the net the cube is made from. Use the net to work out the letters that should go on each face of the cube.

Write the correct letters on the faces.

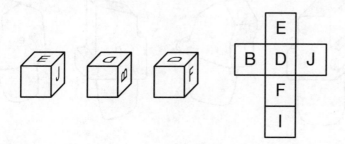

Now use the letters you've written to work out the answer to the riddle below.

Note: The letters are mixed up so you'll need to rearrange them to solve the riddle.

What has one head, one foot and four legs? a _____ _____ _____

Shape Sudoku

Instead of using numbers, our Sudoku uses shapes. The grid is divided into sections, each having four squares. You can also see that there is a net of a cube in the grid (which is shaded).

Finish the Sudoku.

Note: In Sudoku, each column, each row and each of the four sections needs to have one of the four shapes.

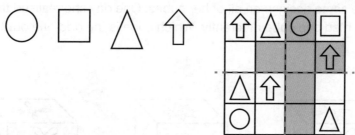

Now use the net to complete these cubes.

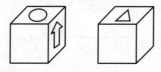

89

Puzzle 3

2D views and cubes

Yes, Chef!

Here are five chefs wearing their 3D chef hats. Try to match each chef to their 2D hat from the selection below. Write the letter of the chef on the correct 2D hat.

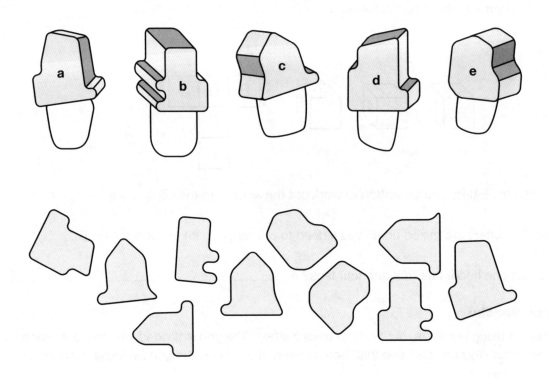

Odd one out

Ms Potter paints the same designs on all of her cubes. One day she realised that she had made a mistake and had painted one cube differently. Which cube is the odd one out?

Puzzle 4

Complete 3D block and fold/punch

Hide and seek

Kim made a shape from some building blocks. Her little sister pulled it apart into three pieces and hid the white piece. Can you spot which is the missing piece?

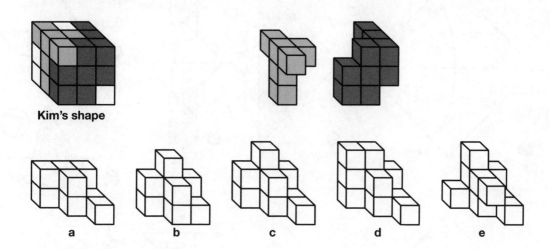

Kim's shape

a   b   c   d   e

Paper decorations

Chloe is making paper decorations to hang in the window of her bedroom. She folds the paper, as shown below. Then she cuts out some shapes.

In the blank square, draw in how Chloe's paper decorations will look when unfolded.

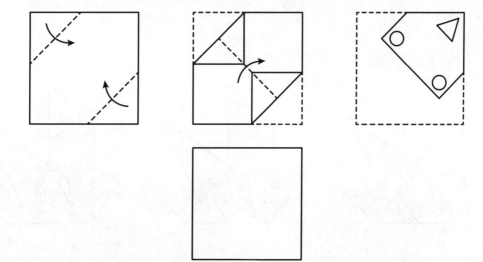

Puzzle 5

Folding on a line

Origami

These paper-folding instructions show how to make a bird. But which bird do they make? Draw a circle around your answer.

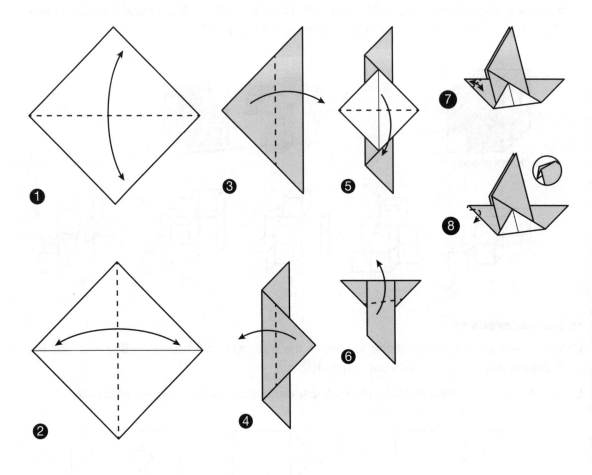

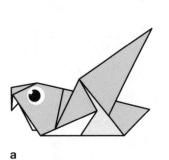

a

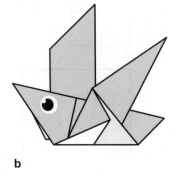

b

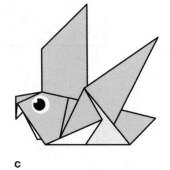

c

Puzzle 6 Rotation of 3D blocks

The creature

Dr Frankenstein wants to build a creature like the one shown below. He's collected different body parts and is ready to get started. Draw a circle around the body parts that will build the creature. Some will need to be rotated.

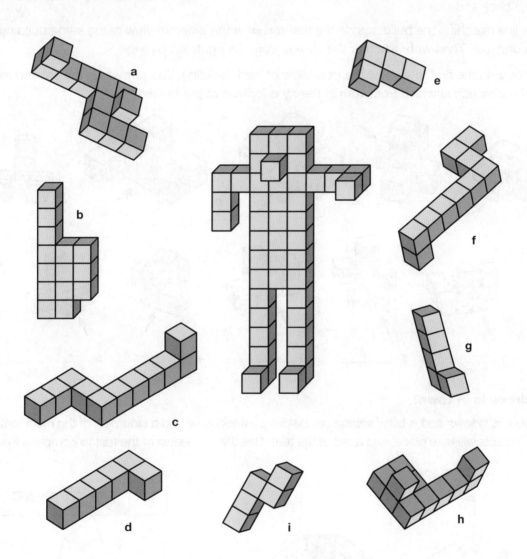

a

e

b

f

g

c

d

i

h

Puzzle 7 — 3D views and shaded nets

Special delivery

Postwoman Penny has to deliver some important packages but the road is blocked. She must go a different way. She knows what the front of each building looks like, but she has to identify them from the back and sides.

Draw a line matching the buildings on the first row with the different view of the same buildings on the second row. Then write whether the view is from the right, left or back.

The arrows on the first row show the front view of each building. The arrows on the second row show the direction in which Postwoman Penny is looking at the buildings.

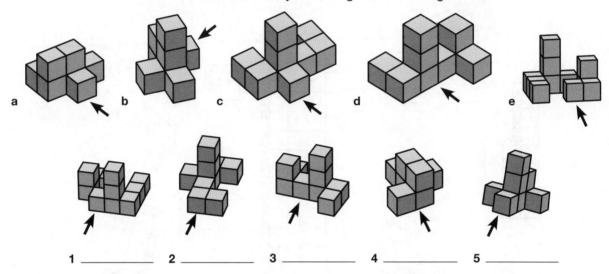

1 _____ 2 _____ 3 _____ 4 _____ 5 _____

The circus is in town!

The circus is in town and is busy setting up. Below are a top view and a side view of the main tent where the acts will take place, and a net of the tent. Use the two views of the tent to complete the net.

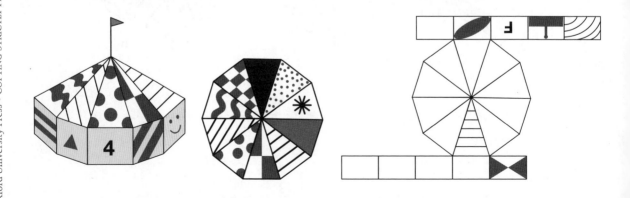

Puzzle 8   Fold and punch and nets and cubes

Paper lantern

Here are some instructions for making a paper lantern. If you were to follow the instructions, folding the paper as shown, which lantern would you end up with?

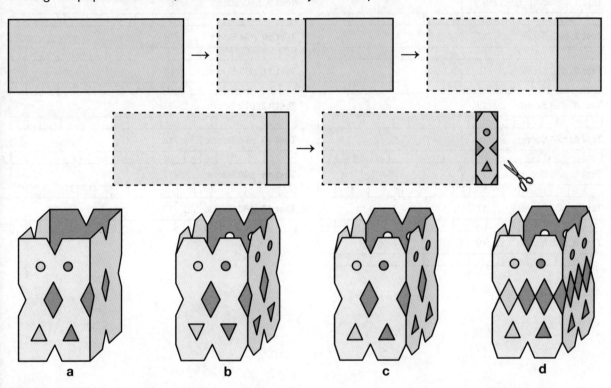

a   b   c   d

Number time

The numbers 1 to 6 are on the faces of this cube. When the cube was rolled on the paper track, copies of the numbers were left on the paper, but some numbers were missing.

Use the net to work out the numbers that go in the empty spaces. (Numbers are shown not actual way up.)

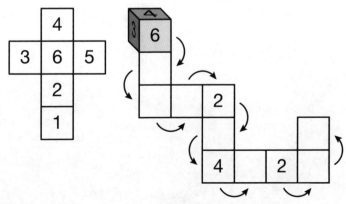

Progress chart

How did you do? Fill in your score below and shade in the corresponding boxes to compare your progress across the different tests.

50%　　　　　　100%　　　　　　　　50%　　　　　　100%

Test 1, p8 Score: _____ /19

Test 9, p60 Score: _____ /16

Test 2, p12 Score: _____ /17

Test 10, p64 Score: _____ /18

Test 3, p16 Score: _____ /16

Test 11, p68 Score: _____ /18

Test 4, p20 Score: _____ /19

Test 12, p72 Score: _____ /17

Test 5, p24 Score: _____ /16

Test 13, p76 Score: _____ /18

Test 6, p28 Score: _____ /17

Test 14, p80 Score: _____ /17

Test 7, p32 Score: _____ /17

Test 15, p84 Score: _____ /19

Test 8, p36 Score: _____ /19